Introduction

This book is designed to help you to get ready for a post-16 course in physics: A level, A/S level, B TEC. Scottish Higher etc. The precise course you will be following doesn't matter because this book stresses the principles of physics which are the same for any course. You could use it before you begin your advanced course or during the first part of that course.* It should also be useful for reference during your studies – especially the chapter on mathematics background. *Access to Advanced Level: Physics* has been designed so that you can work through it on your own, and the answers to all the questions are at the end of each chapter. However, cheating won't help your understanding!

How to use this book

Teaching yourself how to do something needs confidence, and often that is the one thing that you don't have. We suggest that you work through each section slowly and don't move on to the next section until you have correctly answered the questions. If you are getting most of them right you are doing well. What if you aren't? One resource is a standard physics textbook. One of the skills you will have to develop for advanced study is independent learning. There is a variety of approaches to explaining concepts and ours may not always be the best for you. At advanced level (and beyond), referring to text books and reading on your own initiative is going to give you a valuable skill and that essential ingredient, **confidence**, in your ability to learn by yourself.

Good luck and enjoy your physics!

The authors and editors

*There is a glossary of important terms at the back of the book for you to refer to.

Chapter 1   Atomic and nuclear physics

Starting points

Do you understand the following terms:
**atom, proton, neutron, electron, nucleus,
energy**? Write a sentence or two (no more)
to explain what you understand by each
term. Then check in the glossary.

The structure of the atom

Scientists believe that atoms are made up of three main particles: the
proton, the neutron and the electron. Their properties are
summarised in Table 1.1.

Table 1.1 – Sub-atomic particles

	Proton	Neutron	Electron
approximate mass in u *	1	1	1/1840 (approximately 0)
electric charge	+1	0	−1

* 1 u is approximately 1.6×10^{-27} kg

Rutherford's model of the atom

A useful model of the atom was proposed by Ernest Rutherford in 1911. He
suggested that all of the positive charge and all of the mass were concentrated
in a very small volume, or nucleus, at the centre of the atom. The negative
electrons were imagined to be outside the nucleus and most of the atom was
considered to be empty space, see Fig 1.1 (not drawn to scale).

Evidence for this suggestion was provided by an experiment in which alpha
particles were directed at a very thin (1/1000 mm) sheet of gold foil, see Fig 1.2
(not drawn to scale). Most of the alpha particles went straight through but a few
(about 1 in every 8000) were reflected back.

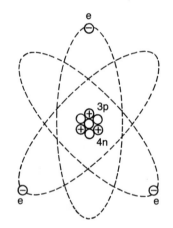

1.1   Model of lithium atom.

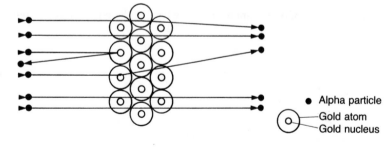

● Alpha particle
○ Gold atom
Gold nucleus

1.2   Scattering of alpha
particles from gold foil.

Neutrons and protons

Further experiments, which involved bombarding the nucleus with
fast moving particles, suggested that the nucleus contained two types
of particle. These were the positively-charged proton and the neutral
particle or neutron. The masses of these are approximately the same.

Access to Advanced Level Physics

Dave Bush

Steve Carpenter

Mary Edwards

Series editors:
Ted Lister and Janet Renshaw,
Trinity School, Leamington Spa

SIMON & SCHUSTER
EDUCATION

Contents

Acknowledgements

The authors and editors would like to thank Bob Drumgoole, their colleague at Trinity School, for reading and making helpful comments on early drafts of this book. They would also like to thank pupils at Trinity School for trialling some of the material.

The authors and publishers would like to thank the following for permission to reproduce photographs. J Champion/Royal Society: Fig 1.4; N Feather/Science Photo Library: Fig 1.3: Llowarch's *Ripple Tank Studies in Wave Motion*, Oxford University Press: Figs 6.9(a), 6.9(b), 6.10(a), 6.10(b), 6.13; Richards, Sears, Wehr and Zermansky, *Modern College Physics*, Addison-Wesley: Fig 6.11(b); Claire Starkey: Fig 1.5.

Text © D Bush, S Carpenter, M Edwards, T Lister, J Renshaw

Design and artwork © Simon & Schuster 1992

First published in 1992 in Great Britain by
Simon and Schuster Education
Campus 400, Maylands Avenue
Hemel Hempstead, Herts HP2 7EZ

Reprinted in 1993

A catalogue record for this book is available from the British Library

ISBN 07501 02667

Typeset by Jim Weaver Design
Illustrated by Tek-Art
Printed in Great Britain by St Edmundsbury Press Ltd
Bury St Edmunds, Suffolk

Mass number and atomic number

The mass number of an atom, sometimes given the symbol A, is the total number of nucleons (neutrons and protons) that it contains. The atomic number, sometimes given the symbol Z, is the number of protons. This is often shown in this way:

Mass no.   23

    Symbol for element   eg   Na   for the atom sodium

Atomic no.   11

Symbols for the elements can be found in the Periodic Table. Some examples are given in Table 1.2.

Table 1.2 – The first six elements

Atomic number	Element	Symbol
1	hydrogen	$^{1}_{1}\text{H}$
2	helium	$^{4}_{2}\text{He}$
3	lithium	$^{7}_{3}\text{Li}$
4	beryllium	$^{9}_{4}\text{Be}$
5	boron	$^{11}_{5}\text{B}$
6	carbon	$^{12}_{6}\text{C}$

1 Look at the following list of elements and answer the questions.

$$^{27}_{13}\text{Al} \quad ^{75}_{33}\text{As} \quad ^{9}_{4}\text{Be} \quad ^{133}_{55}\text{Cs}$$

a How many protons are in each nucleus?

b Work out how many neutrons are in each nucleus.

c Bearing in mind that the whole atom is neutral, write down the number of electrons present in each atom.

Isotopes

Different atoms of the same element can have the same atomic number but a different mass number. This must mean that they each have the same number of protons but a different number of neutrons. These atoms are called **isotopes**. They behave chemically in the same way but have different masses. Chemical behaviour depends on the number of electrons which, in a neutral atom, is the same as the number of protons.

2 Identify the two pairs of isotopes from the following. X is written instead of each atom's symbol.

$$^{12}_{6}\text{X} \quad ^{16}_{8}\text{X} \quad ^{17}_{8}\text{X} \quad ^{14}_{6}\text{X}$$

Nuclear radiation

The nuclei of some atoms give off one or more types of radiation. This radiation can knock electrons out of other atoms (ionise them). This ionisation enables us to detect the radiation.

Ionisation

When an atom is ionised one of its outer electrons is removed. This leaves a positively-charged particle called a positive **ion**. Energy is required to pull the negative electron away from the positive nucleus. This is called the **ionisation energy** of the atom. The values of the ionisation energy, in electronvolts, for some atoms, are given in Table 1.3.

The electronvolt (symbol eV) is a convenient energy unit for very small amounts of energy. One joule of energy is approximately six million million million electronvolts.

Table 1.3   Ionisation energies of some elements

Atom	Ionisation energy in eV
lithium	4.6
beryllium	9.4
magnesium	7.5
argon	15.7
xenon	12.1

3 Suggest what factors might affect the ease with which an electron can be removed from an atom.

The cloud chamber

A cloud chamber shows up the path of ionising radiation. The air inside the chamber is saturated with vapour. When the radiation passes through, it leaves ions in its wake. The vapour condenses on these ions, forming tiny droplets. These droplets indicate the path taken by the ions. This is rather like the condensation trail of an aircraft.

The radiation itself uses up energy every time it ionises an atom. There is, therefore, a maximum length of track depending on the energy of the particular radiation.

1.3   Photograph of alpha particle tracks in a cloud chamber.

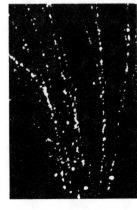

Nuclei give out different types of radiation which can be recognised from the kinds of track they produce. They are named after letters of the Greek alphabet. Have a look at Figs 1.3 and 1.4.

In Fig 1.3, the tracks are thick and straight. They are caused by **alpha radiation**. In Fig 1.4, the thin tracks are caused by **beta radiation**.

1.4   Photograph of beta particle tracks in a cloud chamber.

4 Alpha radiation produces more ions per centimetre travelled than does beta radiation. It also travels more slowly. Use this information to explain the differences in the tracks alpha radiation and beta radiation make in the cloud chamber.

The Geiger-Müller tube

This instrument, see Figs 1.5 and 1.6, is used to 'count' radioactive particles.The particles enter through the thin window and cause ionisation of the gas atoms inside the tube. This produces Ar^+ ions and electrons. The negative electrons are attracted by the positive central wire and accelerate towards it while the positive ions move towards the inner wall of the tube. If the voltage between the central wire and the walls is large enough, then these particles will ionise atoms on the way. Thus an avalanche of moving charge is created. It is this avalanche which is registered to indicate that a particle of ionising radiation has passed into the tube.

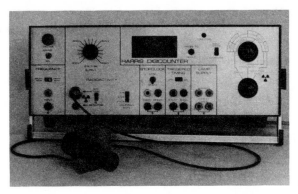

1.5 The Geiger-Müller tube.

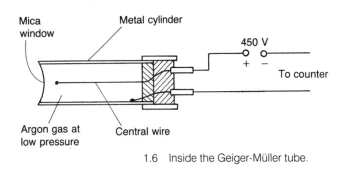

1.6 Inside the Geiger-Müller tube.

Types of radiation

Look back at the cloud chamber photographs, Figs 1.3 and 1.4. The different types of tracks are caused by the different properties of the radiation which passes through. We can identify three types of nuclear radiation. These are **alpha radiation**, symbol, α; **beta radiation**, symbol β; and **gamma radiation**, symbol, γ.

Alpha radiation

This can be stopped by a thick sheet of paper, your clothing or even your skin. It will travel only a few centimetres in air, and it causes intense ionisation of the gas molecules because it collides with them so often. It can be deflected from a straight line path by an electric or magnetic field. The size and direction of these deflections suggest that alpha radiation consists of particles with a particular mass and charge. The mass and charge are the same as those of a helium ion, He^{2+}. In fact, Rutherford collected the gas formed when alpha particles were trapped in a tube and showed that it was helium.

So, an alpha particle is simply a particle composed of two neutrons and two protons which is thrown out of the nucleus of the original atom.

5 Write down the mass number and the atomic number for an alpha particle. Hint: look at Table 1.2.

1.7   The deflections of alpha, beta and gamma radiation in a magnetic field.

Beta radiation

This has a greater range than alpha radiation and can actually travel several metres in air. It will pass through paper but can be stopped by a few millimetres of aluminium. It produces fewer ions per centimetre of travel than does alpha radiation. The sizes and directions of the deflections of beta radiation in magnetic (see Fig 1.7) and electric fields show that beta radiation consists of fast-moving electrons. So the beta particle is much less massive than an alpha particle (about 1/7000) and carries a single negative charge.

Gamma radiation

This is extremely penetrating. It is not completely stopped even by several centimetres of lead. It produces fewer ions per centimetre of travel than does beta radiation of comparable energy and far fewer than does comparable alpha radiation. It is not deflected by electric or magnetic fields, which suggests that it is not charged. It is possible, however, to show both **interference** and **diffraction** with gamma radiation. This suggests that it consists of waves (see Chapter 6).

In fact, gamma radiation is very short wavelength **electromagnetic waves** and it travels at the speed of light.

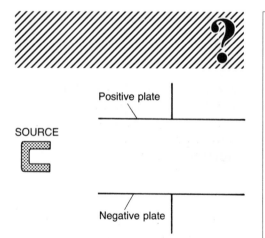

1.8   Radiation travelling through an electric field.

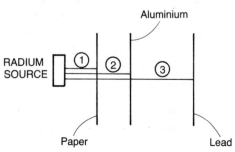

1.9   Absorption of radiation.

6 Make an enlarged copy of the apparatus shown in Fig 1.8 and sketch the paths you would expect alpha, beta and gamma radiation to follow.

7 Can you identify which type of radiation is which in Fig 1.9?

8 Re-read the paragraphs above and extract the following information. Which type of radiation:
   a has a positive charge?
   b is the most penetrating?
   c is most easily deflected by a magnetic field?
   d consists of waves?
   e causes the most intense ionisation per centimetre of travel?
   f has the shortest range in air?
   g has a negative charge?
   h is not deflected by an electric field?

Nuclear transformations

Since all of these different types of radiation come out of the nucleus, then the composition of the nucleus must be affected when radiation is given off. We say that the nucleus has decayed.

Alpha decay

Radium, for example, gives out an alpha particle. This must mean a loss of two protons and two neutrons from the nucleus.

This can be expressed using the atomic number and the mass number in a so-called nuclear equation.

$$^{226}_{88}\text{Ra} \rightarrow \ ^{222}_{86}\text{Rn} + \ ^{4}_{2}\text{He}$$

The number of protons in the nucleus has been reduced from 88 to 86, while the total number of nucleons has been reduced from 226 to 222. This means that a different element has been produced. In this case the new element has atomic number 86, which is radon, symbol Rn.

Notice that the top numbers balance on each side of the equation as do the bottom numbers. The nuclear equation deals only with the particles in the nucleus not with the electrons.

9 Radon-222 is a gas which is radioactive. It decays to polonium, Po, by giving out an alpha particle. Write down the nuclear equation to describe this transformation.

Beta decay

Beta decay is a little more complicated. There are no electrons in the nucleus. What happens is that one of the neutrons changes into a proton plus an electron. The proton stays in the nucleus and the electron is emitted as a beta particle.

This means that the atomic number (the number of protons) actually increases by one. The total mass number remains the same, since a proton has approximately the same mass as a neutron and the mass of an electron is so small that we can neglect it.

Thorium-234 decays to protactinium-234 by emitting a beta particle. The nuclear equation will be

$$^{234}_{90}\text{Th} \rightarrow \ ^{234}_{91}\text{Pa} + \ ^{0}_{-1}\text{e}$$

$^{0}_{-1}\text{e}$ stands for a beta particle, since it has a mass of zero and a charge of −1.

10 Write down the nuclear equations for the following transformations:

a lead-211 to bismuth-211

b francium-221 to astatine-217

c plutonium-241 to americium-241

d thorium-231 to protactinium-231

You will need the following symbols and atomic numbers: lead, Pb, 82; bismuth, Bi, 83; francium, Fr, 87; astatine, At, 85; americium, Am, 95; plutonium, Pu, 94; thorium, Th, 90; protactinium, Pa, 91.

Fission and fusion

The protons and neutrons in atomic nuclei are held together by the strong nuclear force – the strongest known force. This means that they have locked up in them a great deal of energy. In the case of some heavy nuclei such as uranium they can split into parts with a release of some of this energy. This process is called **nuclear fission**. It is the source of the energy generated in nuclear reactors.

Light nuclei such as hydrogen can join together with release of energy in a process called **nuclear fusion**. This is the source of the energy produced by the Sun and in the hydrogen bomb.

Radioactive decay

The changes which occur when a radioactive substance decays are not like chemical changes. They are spontaneous and cannot be controlled. They are not affected by physical conditions such as temperature or pressure, neither are they affected by the element involved being chemically combined. Also, the energy released in radioactive decay processes is enormously greater than that in chemical changes.

The chance nature of radioactive decay

The chance of any one radioactive atom decaying can be compared to the chance of throwing a six with a die. Imagine throwing 3600 dice to represent radioactive atoms. About 1/6 (600) would show a six. Let these represent the atoms which have decayed and remove them. Throw the remaining 3000 again. Once more about 1/6 (this time, 500) will show a six. Remove these and throw again, and so on. The number removed at each throw will decrease by about 1/6 of the previous number removed. This is shown on the graph, Fig 1.10. This type of graph showing steady decrease by a constant ratio (1/6 in our example) is called **exponential**. Although there is a predictable pattern, it is still impossible to predict that one individual die will show a six at any time.

The same rule applies to nuclei. It is impossible to specify when a *particular* nucleus will decay but, if a large sample is taken, the number which have decayed in each second plotted against time, will give an exponential graph shaped like the one in Fig 1.10.

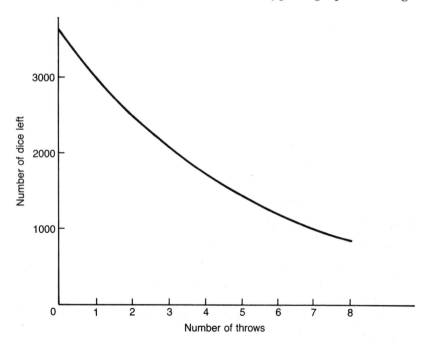

1.10   A graph showing exponential decay.

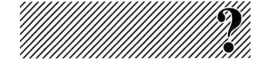

11 Simulation of radioactive decay. Collect together as many coins as possible – at least 60. Throw them on the floor and remove those which land heads up (these represent the atoms which have decayed). Count the remainder and enter the number in Table 1.4. Throw the remaining coins again, remove the heads and enter the number remaining in the Table. Continue until no coins remain. Plot a graph of number of coins remaining (vertically) against the throw number (horizontally). Compare your graph with the one in Fig 1.10.

Table 1.4 – Simulation of radioactive decay

Throw number	Number of coins remaining
0	60
1	
2	
3	
4	
5	
6	

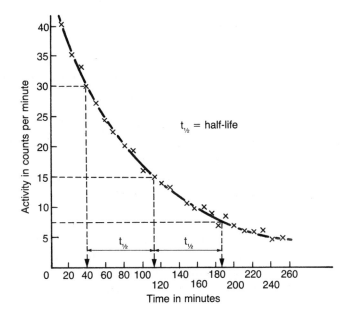

1.11 The half-life of this substance is 73 minutes.

The number of nuclei which decay in one second is called the **activity** of the source (the greater the activity, the more radioactive the source). A close look at the graph in Fig 1.11 shows that the time taken for the activity to reduce by half is always the same. This time is called the **half-life** and it can vary from fractions of a second up to millions of years depending on the element. The half-life of a radioactive source can be found using a graph as shown in Fig 1.11.

12 The results shown in Table 1.5 are from an experiment to measure the activity of a radio-active element at different times.

a Plot a graph of activity (vertically) against time (horizontally).

b Use this graph to find the half-life of the substance.

c After three half-lives, what would you expect for the value of the activity of the substance? Show how you arrive at this value.

Table 1.5 – Radioactive decay

Time in minutes	Activity in counts per second
0.0	1340
1.0	834
1.8	584
3.0	340
5.0	134

Background radiation

The results given in Table 1.5 were taken using a Geiger-Müller tube. This will count *all* the radiation entering it, not just that from the source in which we are interested. Radiation from radioactive materials in rocks and air and also cosmic rays, will all be counted. This is called **background radiation**. To find the actual activity of the source we must subtract this background radiation from each of the measured counts. We can measure the background radiation by taking a count without the source present. In question 12 above, the background count was 4 counts per second so the observed count at time 0 would have been 1344 counts per second.

> 13 Work out the actual observed count rate for the reading taken after 3.0 minutes, in question 12.

Radiocarbon dating

The carbon present in the carbon dioxide in the atmosphere contains a small proportion of the radioactive isotope carbon-14. Knowing the half-life of this substance means that the age of material which has once lived can be determined. All material that is living, or has once lived, contains carbon. The amount of radioactive carbon reduces with time as it decays, but in a living substance the carbon is continually replaced by respiration. This means that a certain amount of living material always contains a constant and unchanging amount of radioactive carbon.

When the material dies, however, the carbon is no longer replaced and hence the amount of radioactive carbon *does* reduce with time. The activity of radioactive carbon in living material is approximately 16 counts per minute for every gram of carbon. Carbon-14 has a half-life of approximately 5600 years.

A wooden carving is found whose carbon-14 activity is two counts per minute per gram of wood. What is its age?

When the wood died, the carbon-14 activity would have been 16 counts per minute per gram. This will reduce by half every 5600 years. So after 5600 years the activity would have been 8 counts per minute per gram; 5600 years later still, 4 counts per minute per gram; and a further 5600 years later, 2 counts per minute per gram. Thus, the age of the carving must be

5600 + 5600 + 5600 = 16 800 years

14 A piece of wood found in an archaeological excavation can be radiocarbon dated. Use the following steps to find its age:

a What would you expect the activity of 5 grams of carbon in the living wood to be?

b When 5 grams of the carbon from the excavated wood was tested, the activity was found to be 20 counts per minute. Can you suggest an approximate age for the wood?

Answers

1 a 13, 33, 4, 55   b 14, 42, 5, 78   c 13, 33, 4, 55

2 $^{16}_{8}X$ and $^{17}_{8}X$; $^{14}_{6}X$ and $^{12}_{6}X$

3 The number of protons in the nucleus – more protons will hold the electron more tightly. The distance of the electrons from the nucleus – the closer they are, the more tightly they will be held.

4 An alpha particle spends more time in one area so it can affect more of the atoms. Therefore, lots of ions form causing a thick track of droplets.

5 Atomic mass = 4,   atomic number = 2

6

Positive plate

SOURCE

Beta particles

Gamma rays

Alpha particles

Negative plate   (Not to scale)

1.12   Beta particles are deflected 4000 times more than alpha particles.

7 1 is α,   2 is β,   3 is γ

8 a α   b γ   c β   d γ   e α   f α   g β   h γ

9 $^{222}_{86}Rn \rightarrow\ ^{218}_{84}Po + ^{4}_{2}He$

10 a $^{211}_{82}Pb \rightarrow\ ^{211}_{83}Bi + ^{0}_{-1}e$

b $^{221}_{87}Fr \rightarrow\ ^{217}_{85}At + ^{4}_{2}He$

c $^{241}_{94}Pu \rightarrow\ ^{241}_{95}Am + ^{0}_{-1}e$

d $^{231}_{90}Th \rightarrow\ ^{231}_{91}Pa + ^{0}_{-1}e$

11 Your graph should be the same basic shape as that in Fig 1.10, but it may well not be as smooth. This will depend on how many coins you used.

12 a

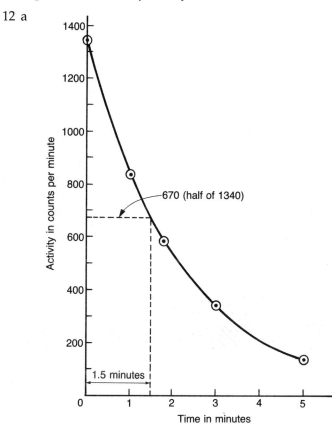

1.13

b 1.5 minutes – see graph in Fig 1.13.

c 1340/8 = 167.5 counts per minute

13 344 counts per second

14 a 16 × 5 = 80 counts per minute

b This is 1/4 of the rate for the living wood, so it must be two half-lives old ie   2 × 5600 = 11 200 years.

Chapter 2

Energy

Do you understand the following terms: **energy, work, force**? Write a sentence or two (no more) to explain what you understand by each term. Then check in the glossary.

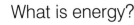

What is energy?

Energy is that rather nebulous 'stuff that makes things go'. We say something has energy if it has the ability to move a **force** (a push or a pull) – for example to lift a weight or push a car. Energy is the ability to do **work**.

1 Select from the list* below the type of energy possessed by:
a a speeding bullet
b a hot water bottle
c a lump of coal
d a charged car battery
e a lump of uranium
f a skier at the top of a slope

* heat energy, kinetic energy, electrical energy, chemical energy, gravitational potential energy, nuclear energy

Work

Whenever a force moves an object (in its own direction) a physicist says that it is doing work. Here we are using an everyday word (work) in a special sense. In physics, work only means moving the point of action of a force. So thinking about your homework is not doing work in the physics sense, but playing tennis is. A shelf holding up some books is providing a force, but as it not moving, the shelf is doing no work.

2 In which of the following situations is work being done?
a An executive making decisions.
b A pillar holding up a bridge.
c A weightlifter making a lift.
d A hockey player scoring a goal.
e Your chair, holding you off the floor.

Measuring work

The harder you push, the more work you do.
The further you push, the more work you do.
The amount of work, W, depends on:
the size of the force, F (measured in newtons)
the distance it moves, d (measured in metres)

So, Work = force × distance
     W   = F   × d

The units of work are therefore newton metres which are called joules. It takes a force of about 1 newton to lift an average-sized apple. So if you lift an apple from the kitchen floor on to a 1 m high worktop, you have done 1 joule of work and transferred 1 joule of your energy to the apple. As energy is transformed, work is being done. Work and energy have the same units. Energy can be compared to having money in your pocket, whilst work can be compared to spending it.

How much work is done in pushing a car 1500 m with a force of 400 N?

$$W = F \times d$$
$$W = 400 \text{ N} \times 1500 \text{ m}$$
$$W = 600\,000 \text{ J}$$

3 A cyclist pushes her bicycle with a force of 200 N for a distance of 6320 m. How much work does she do?

4 A car uses 8000 J of energy in moving 20 m. With how much force does the engine push the car?

5 A motorcycle has 60 000 J of movement energy. If the brakes deliver a stopping force of 500 N, what is the shortest distance the motorcyclist can stop in?

2.1   A lump of coal can do work.

Anything that has energy has the ability to do work as defined above. For example, see Fig 2.1, a lump of coal can be burnt to run a steam engine which could lift a load. The bigger the energy content of the coal, the more work it could do. So the ability to do work is how we measure how much energy something has.

The test of whether something has energy is whether it has the ability to do some work (move a force).

The conservation of energy

Einstein's famous equation, $E = mc^2$, tells us that mass and energy can be converted into each other, so to be strictly accurate we should talk about the conservation of mass/energy.

The outcome of vast numbers of experiments over many years has led to the idea that we can neither create energy from nothing nor destroy it. We say that energy is conserved and call this rule the **Law of Conservation of Energy**. It is one of the most basic laws of science. We can transform energy from one form to another but the total amount remains the same.

James Prescott Joule

James Joule was the son of a brewer. He began to study different forms of energy at the age of only 19. He established that heat and electricity were both forms of energy and could be made to do work (by lifting loads). He made many very careful measurements of different types of energy which led to the idea that it is always conserved. He was a somewhat modest man and spent some time working as an assistant to Lord Kelvin. Both men had units named after them – the unit of temperature (the kelvin) and the unit of energy (the joule).

Energy transfers

Simply having energy is not much use. Energy is only useful when it is transformed into some other form. A charged battery is not much good in itself, but it is useful if it supplies energy to an electric motor which is running, say, a milk float.

As was said earlier, energy and money are similar in many ways. Money is no use sitting in your purse or wallet: it only works for you when you spend it. Even then it is not destroyed, it is simply transferred to someone else.

Types of energy

The question at the beginning of the chapter lists six types of energy. It is useful if we can measure the amounts of different types of energy that we are dealing with.

Gravitational potential energy

This is the type of energy an object has when it is raised above the ground. We can see how to measure the amount of gravitational potential energy that an object has by thinking about how much work we had to do to get it there. For example, imagine carrying a rucksack to the top of a flight of stairs. Your work to get it (and you) to the top would differ with the mass of the sack and the height of the flight of stairs. The other important factor is the gravitational pull of the Earth.

Measuring gravitational potential energy

The Earth's gravitational field strength (usually given the symbol g) is about 10 N/kg. So to lift a mass of 1 kg requires a force of about 10 N.

Suppose we have a mass of 20 kg , a distance of 5 m above the Earth's surface. How much work was done to get it there?

To lift a mass of 20 kg requires a force, F, of 20 kg $\times$ 10 N/kg = 200 N

$$\text{Work} = \text{force} \times \text{distance}$$
$$W = F \times d$$
So, $$W = 200\,N \times 5\,m$$
$$W = 1000\,J$$

In other words, the work done, which is now the potential energy of the mass, is 1000 J.

Now the force F = mg and the distance it has moved is the height, h.

In general, the gravitational potential energy, PE, of a mass, m, in a gravitational field, g, at a height, h, above the surface is given by:

$$PE = mgh$$

Notice that we are using the Earth's surface as a zero of energy. We could use any zero, but this is quite convenient.

A weightlifter raises 250 kg through 2 m. If the gravitational field strength is 10 N/kg, how much energy does the mass gain?

$$PE = mgh$$
$$PE = 250\,kg \times 10\,N/kg \times 2\,m$$
$$PE = 5000\,J$$

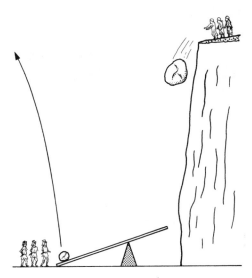

2.2 Testing a Roman catapult.

(Take g = 10 N/kg throughout)

6 How much energy is needed to carry a toddler of mass 11 kg from road level to the 12th floor of a building 36m above?

7 A catapult has 20 J of energy to project a marble of mass 0.005 kg upwards. What is the maximum height the marble can reach above the catapult?

8 The water from a hydroelectric power station can release 40×10^6 J of energy falling through 40 m. What mass of water must be used in this process?

9 A golf ball can be thrown 40 m up into the air on Earth. How many times higher could it be thrown on the Moon where the gravity is only 1.6 N/kg? Hint: assume the ball gains the same amount of PE in each case.

10 A Roman catapult (Fig 2.2) relied on a heavy mass falling on to a pivoted beam, to launch a smaller mass into the air. If a mass of 200 kg is allowed to fall 3 m, how much PE did the mass have before it fell? What is the largest mass it could launch over a wall 10 m high if no energy is wasted?

Kinetic energy

Clearly, moving objects have energy. The energy of movement is often called kinetic energy, the word coming from the same root as the word cinema (moving pictures). The amount of kinetic energy, KE, objects have depends on their velocity, v, and their mass, m, and is given by the equation

$$KE = \tfrac{1}{2}mv^2$$

A car of mass 750 kg is moving at a velocity of 10 m/s. What is its kinetic energy?

$$KE = \tfrac{1}{2}mv^2$$
$$KE = 750 \text{ kg} \times 10 \text{ m/s} \times 10 \text{ m/s}/2$$
$$KE = 37\,500 \text{ J}$$

11 What is the KE of a runner with a mass of 80 kg, travelling at 10 m/s?

12 If a 40 000 kg truck is travelling at 30 m/s, what is its KE?

13 A Rounders' ball is thrown with a velocity of 25 m/s. What is its KE if its mass is 0.3 kg?

14 If a skateboarder of mass 50 kg has a KE of 1600 J, how fast is she going?

15 A motorbike, when travelling at 20 m/s has a KE of 50 000 J. What is the mass of the bike?

Did you know that water has a very high specific heat capacity? This makes it an excellent liquid for hot water bottles.

Heat energy

The amount of energy stored in a hot object depends on its temperature, its mass and also the material it is made of – some materials store more heat than others. The ability of a material to store heat is measured by the specific heat capacity, c. It tells us how much heat energy has been stored in 1 kg of the material when it has been heated by 1 °C. It is measured in J/kg/°C.

We can only use the energy stored in a hot body by transferring it to a colder body, so in heat energy problems we deal with heat *change*. When dealing with an object being heated up or cooled down, we can use the equation:

Heat energy transferred = mcθ

where   m is the mass of object;   c is the specific heat capacity;
θ is the temperature change.

A saucepan of water is heated from 20 °C to 100 °C. The specific heat capacity of water is 4200 kJ/kg/°C. The mass of the water is 2 kg. How much heat energy, HE, is stored in the water?

$$HE = mc\theta$$
$$HE = 2 \text{ kg} \times 4200 \text{ J/kg/°C} \times 80 \text{ °C}$$
$$HE = 672\,000 \text{ J}$$

16 How much energy is required to heat a room of air, mass 24 kg, by 15 °C? The specific heat capacity of air is 100 J/kg/°C.

17 A storage heater requires 84×10^6 J to heat it by 20 °C. If its mass is 100 kg, what is the specific heat capacity of the storage material?

18 A brick of mass 2 kg is heated from 60 °C to 70 °C. If the specific heat capacity of brick is 8400 J/kg/°C, how much energy is used to heat it?

Electrical energy

When electric charge flows through a component in a circuit, electrical energy is converted into some other form, or forms. The amount of energy, E, converted is given by

$$E = QV \quad \text{or} \quad E = ItV$$

where
Q is the charge which flows, in coulombs
V is the the potential difference across the component, in volts
I is the current flowing, in amps
t is the time, in seconds

See Chapter 4 for more details.

19 How much energy is used by an electric motor which is run at 240 V for 1 minute, if it draws a current of 7 A?

20 750 J of energy are given to a hair dryer in 3 s. If the hair dryer operates at 250 V, what current does it draw?

21 A current of 10 A is delivered to a kettle for 3 minutes. If this delivers 420 000 J, what potential difference does the kettle run at?

22 A torch bulb draws a current of 0.3 A from a 1.5 V battery. How long would it take to use 100 J of energy?

23 If a 1.2 V rechargeable battery stores 2700 J of electrical energy, for how much longer would it run a 2.7 W bulb than a 3.1 W bulb?

Power

Sometimes we are interested, not just in how much energy we need to convert for a particular purpose, but also how fast we can do it. For example, it takes 1 000 000 J to move a lift of mass 1000 kg (including its occupants) to the top of a 100 m building. (You might like to check this using PE = mgh.) Clearly the lift is better if it can do this in 100 s rather than in 200 s.

What we are talking about here is the *rate* of transforming energy. This is called **power**.

$$\text{Power} = \frac{\text{energy transformed}}{\text{time}} \quad \text{or in symbols,} \quad P = \frac{E}{t}$$

The units of power are joules per second, or watts, symbol W.

The power of the faster lift above is 1 000 000 J/ 100 s = 10 000 W. What is the power of the slower one?

What is the power of an engine that uses 12 000 J in 60 s?

P = E/t

P = 12 000 J/60 s

P = 200 W

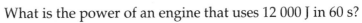

24 The human body delivers 14 000 J of energy in 2 minutes. What is the power of the body?

25 A 60 W light bulb is left on all day. How much energy is used by the bulb?

26 How long would 9 300 000 J of energy power a 600 W motor?

27 A 9000 W motor cycle runs for 30 minutes on 1.2 litres of petrol. For how long would a 20 000 W motor run on the same amount of petrol?

28 A pushbiker uses a dynamo to generate electricity for the lights on her bike. The lights are rated 3 W. If she cycles for an hour, how much energy does she use up generating electricity for her lights?

Efficiency

We have seen that energy is never destroyed. However, when we are transforming energy from one form to another, we almost always fail to convert all the energy we start with into the type of energy we require.

Examples of this include:

- an electric motor, where we convert electrical energy into kinetic energy, but some energy is converted into heat in the wires.
- a power station where we convert the chemical energy of the fuel into electrical energy, but some is lost as heat in the cooling towers and some as sound.

When energy is 'lost' in conversions, it nearly always appears as heat.

The **efficiency** of an energy conversion is the percentage of the energy we put in to a process which comes out in the form we require.

$$\text{Efficiency} = \frac{\text{Useful energy out}}{\text{Energy in}} \times 100\%$$

$$\text{or} \qquad = \frac{\text{Useful power out}}{\text{Useful power in}} \times 100\%$$

A 60 W light bulb delivers only 0.3 W of light. The rest is wasted as heat. What is the efficiency of the light bulb?

$$\text{Efficiency} = \frac{\text{Useful power out}}{\text{Useful power in}} \times 100\%$$

Efficiency = 0.3 W × 100% / 60 W

Efficiency = 0.5%

29 A car uses 16 800 J of chemical energy from its petrol to achieve a kinetic energy of 5200 J. What is the efficiency of the car?

30 An electric motor is only 30% efficient and is rated as using 470 W of electrical energy when working. What is the effective power output of the motor?

31 A pushbike is 75% efficient and a cyclist gains 300 J of movement energy in a fast sprint. How much energy does the cyclist have to put into the bicycle?

32 A steam engine is 20% efficient at converting the chemical energy of coal into heat energy in steam. The pistons are 30% efficient at converting heat in steam into movement energy. If the steam engine has 1 200 000 J of coal fed into it, how much movement energy does it gain?

Answers

1 a kinetic b heat c chemical
  d electrical e nuclear
  f gravitational potential

2 c and d

3 1 264 000 J

4 400 N

5 120 m

6 3960 J

7 400 m

8 100 000 kg

9 250 m (ie 6.25 times higher)

10 6000 J; 60 kg

11 4000 J

12 1.8×10^7 J

13 93.8 J

14 8 m/s

15 250 kg

16 36 000 J

17 42 000 J/kg/°C

18 168 000 J

19 100 800 J

20 1 A

21 233.3 V

22 222.2 s

23 129 s longer
   (871 s as against 1000 s)

24 117 W (to the nearest watt)

25 5.18×10^6 J

26 15 500 s (or 4.3 hours)

27 13.5 minutes

28 10 800 J

29 31%

30 141 W

31 400 J

32 72 000 J

Chapter 3   Motion

Do you understand the following terms:
speed, force, mass? Write a sentence or two
(no more) to explain what you understand
by each. Then check in the glossary.

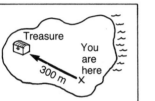

Displacement

Vectors

If you are orienteering and need to know how to get to the next
checkpoint, the information 'it is two miles away' is not much use.
However, 'it is two miles due east' *is* helpful.

The two ideas we need to combine are distance and direction. To
have one piece of information and not the other makes the task

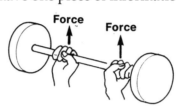

difficult if not impossible. A **vector** is
a piece of information in two parts –
size and direction, and it is usually
shown by an arrow, see Fig 3.1. A
distance which also has its direction
specified is called a **displacement**
and is a vector quantity. Quantities
which have no specified direction are
called **scalars**.

3.1   Vectors have size
and direction.

> 1 Divide the following quantities into vectors and scalars:
>   mass, electric current, temperature, force, volume.

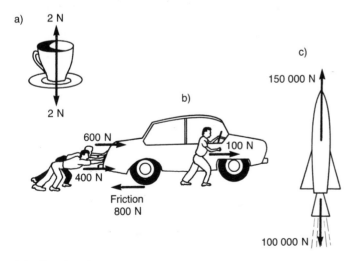

3.2   Resultant forces.

Force

Forces are pushes and pulls which tend to change the
motion or shape of an object. They are vectors
because their direction is clearly important.

If two people are trying to push a car it is more
helpful if both are pushing in the same direction.
Suppose one was pushing a car with a force of
100 newtons forwards at the same time as the other
was pushing it with a force of 60 newtons backwards.
The **resultant** force would be 40 newtons forwards. If
they both pushed forwards with the same forces, the
resultant force would be 160 newtons forwards.

> 2 What is the resultant force in the situations in Fig 3.2?

Speed and velocity

The average **speed** for a journey is the distance travelled divided by the time taken. It is a scalar quantity.

If we also specify the direction, we have a vector quantity, which we call **velocity**.

A car journey from London to Leamington covers 100 miles in two hours.

Average speed = 100 miles / 2 hours
                = 50 miles per hour

Average velocity is 50 miles per hour *in the direction of Leamington.*

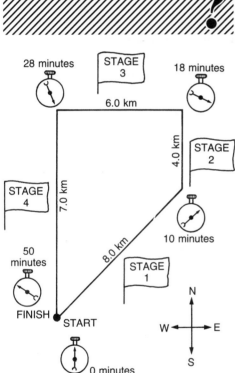

3.3   A charity cycle run.

The symbol Δ is a mathematical shorthand meaning 'change in'.

3 a A cyclist covers 3 km in 6 minutes due South. What is her average velocity?

   b A runner covers 100 m in 10 seconds. What is his average speed?

   c A point on the equator rotates through 24 000 miles in 24 hours. What is its average speed?

The average velocity or speed of an object is useful if we wish to say general things about the journey, but there are times when we need to describe parts of the journey.

A car journey from Banbury to Stratford via Warwick town centre covers the 30 miles in 1 hour. The average speed of the journey is 30 miles per hour but we would expect the car to have to stop several times at roundabouts and traffic lights. This means that if 30 miles per hour is the average speed, there must have been times when the car was travelling faster than 30 miles per hour. We now need a method of calculating the speed or velocity at a particular instant.

$$\text{Velocity over a time interval } = \frac{\text{Change in displacement}}{\text{Change in time}} = \frac{\Delta d}{\Delta t}$$

where d represents the displacement, and t the time taken.

Remember that **displacement** is distance in a specified direction.

As Δt gets smaller, the value of average velocity becomes the instantaneous velocity at a particular instant.

4 You have just completed a charity cycling run and your friend has timed your progress through several stages of the journey. Look at the sketched map in Fig 3.3 and then work out to one significant figure:

   a your average speed for the whole journey
   b your average velocity over each stage.

The winner had an average speed of 0.6 km per minute.

   c During which stage did the winner overtake you?

Changing speed and velocity

We now come to another possible way of expressing average speed. If a car steadily speeds up from 10 m/s to 20 m/s during a journey, then we can describe the car's average speed as:

$$\text{average speed} = \frac{\text{finish speed} + \text{start speed}}{2}$$

Provided the car makes *no change in direction* during the journey,

$$\text{its average velocity} = \frac{v + u}{2}$$

where v represents the velocity at the end of the time interval we are considering and u the velocity at the beginning of this time period.

5 a A runner, on a straight track, steadily increases her speed from 0 m/s to 10 m/s. What is her average velocity?

   b An aircraft goes through the sound barrier by steadily increasing its speed from 250 m/s to 400 m/s. What is its average speed?

   c A car steadily increases its speed from 10 m/s to 40 m/s in 30 s. What is its average speed and how far does it travel while it is increasing its speed?

Acceleration

If the velocity of an object changes, we describe this as an **acceleration**.

$$\text{Acceleration} = \frac{\text{Change in velocity}}{\text{Time taken}}$$

There are two points to note here.

• Since velocity is a vector, a change in velocity could be a change in speed or a change in direction, or both.

• If an object is slowing down, then its acceleration is negative, and is sometimes called deceleration.

In symbol form there are two ways of expressing the acceleration of an object:

See Chapter 7, Vectors, which looks at change in direction.

1) average acceleration, $a = \frac{v - u}{t}$

   v = finish velocity
   u = start velocity
   t = time taken

2) acceleration, $a = \frac{\Delta v}{\Delta t}$

   Δv = change in velocity
   Δt = change in time

In the same way as before, the smaller Δt is, the closer this becomes to the instantaneous acceleration.

The performances of cars are often quoted as their times to go from 0 – 25 m/s (0 – 60 mph). This is supposed to tell us something useful about the car but what does it mean?

A car, travelling in a straight line, accelerates from 0 m/s to 25 m/s in 12.5 s. What is its acceleration?

$$a = \frac{v - u}{t} \text{ where } v = 25 \text{ m/s, } u = 0 \text{ m/s and } t = 12.5 \text{ s}$$

$$a = 25 - 0 \text{ m/s } / 12.5 \text{ s}$$
$$a = 25/12.5 \text{ m/s/s}$$
$$a = 2 \text{ m/s/s}$$

This means that the car speeds up by 2 metres per second, every second.

6 a Work out the accelerations of vehicles on straight tracks, which speed up from 0 – 25 m/s in these times:
   i lorry, 25 s   ii bus, 20 s   iii teacher's car, 15 s
   iv sports car, 8 s   v motorcycle, 3 s

b A pushbike accelerates from 0 to 6 m/s in 2 s on a straight road. What is the acceleration of the pushbike? Compare this with the accelarations of the motor-driven vehicles in the first part of the question.

c If a pushbike's acceleration is so great, why do we use motor-driven vehicles?

d A falling object accelerates at 10 m/s/s. If we start to measure its fall when its speed is 13 m/s, how fast is it going 8 s after this?

Equations of motion

We now have several equations which we can use to describe what is happening to an object while it is moving. Each equation is like a colour on a painting palette. We can outline a picture using one colour but the more colours we have, the better we are able to enhance the picture with detail.

A runner, on a straight track, accelerates steadily from the starting blocks during a race at 2 m/s/s. The runner accelerates for 5 s. What is his velocity when he finishes accelerating? What is his average velocity? How far does he travel in the 5 seconds?

We are dealing with a steady acceleration, so $a = \dfrac{v - u}{t}$

Filling in the values in the equation, $2 \text{ m/s/s} = \dfrac{(v - 0) \text{ m/s}}{5 \text{ s}}$

This gives us an answer of $2 = v / 5$,   so $v = 10$ m/s when he finishes accelerating. We now know the change in velocity.

$$\text{average velocity} \quad = \quad \frac{v + u}{2}$$

$$= \frac{(10 + 0)\ \text{m/s}}{2}$$

average velocity   =   5 m/s while he is accelerating.

The acceleration takes 5 seconds, so now we can work out the distance he travels from the equation:

$$\text{average velocity} \quad = \quad d/t$$

$$5\,\text{m/s} \quad = \quad \frac{d}{5\ \text{seconds}}$$

$$d \quad = \quad 25\,\text{m}$$

So the runner travels 25 m while accelerating.

7 a A stone is dropped from a cliff. It accelerates towards the sea at 10 m/s/s. If it starts from rest and falls for 3 s before hitting the sea, how fast is it travelling when it hits the sea?

   b What is the average velocity of the falling stone?

   c how tall is the cliff?

8 A racing car accelerates steadily from rest at the start line at 6 m/s/s for 10 s. What is its average velocity during acceleration? How far does it travel during acceleration? Assume the car is on a straight track.

Momentum

When an object is moving towards you, the concern you have for your safety depends on how fast the object is moving and how massive it is.

You would certainly step out of the way of a lorry, whereas you might not notice a fly moving at the same speed. The lorry's extra mass means it has greater **momentum** and so is harder to stop.

The momentum, p, of any moving object of mass, m, and velocity, v, is given by

$$\text{momentum} \quad = \quad \text{mass} \times \text{velocity}$$

$$p \quad = \quad mv$$

Since velocity is a vector quantity, so is momentum. The units of momentum are those of mass multiplied by those of velocity so the usual ones are kg m/s.

A 0.01 kg bullet travels at 500 m/s. What is its momentum?

$p = mv$

$p = 0.01 \text{ kg} \times 500 \text{ m/s}$

$p = 5 \text{ kg m/s}$

This is the same as the momentum of a 1 kg brick travelling at 5 m/s. Check that you agree with this.

9 a Calculate the momentum of a 70 kg runner travelling at 10 m/s.

b If a car has a momentum of 12 000 kg m/s and a mass of 1000 kg, how fast is it going?

c A cyclist travelling at 12 m/s has a momentum of 960 kg m/s. What is the mass of the cyclist plus cycle?

d A 0.2 kg cricket ball is thrown at 40 m/s. What is the momentum of the ball?

e If an aircraft has a mass of 50 000 kg and is travelling at 400 m/s, what is its momentum?

Collisions and momentum

Whenever a moving object hits another object then all the momentum before the collision is still there after the collision even if different objects actually have the momentum. We say that the momentum is **conserved**. This enables us to do calculations about moving objects. For example a forensic scientist might be able to calculate the velocity at which a car accident took place. Steve Davis works with momentum instinctively; we might have to do calculations like those in the example. To keep things simple we shall assume that all the collisions take place in a straight line.

A ball of mass 3 kg with a velocity of 2 m/s collides head on with a second ball of mass 2 kg and all the momentum is passed on. What velocity does the second ball move off with if it is initially at rest?

mv before collision $= 3 \text{ kg} \times 2 \text{ m/s} = 6 \text{ kg m/s}$

Since momentum is conserved,

mv after collision $= 6 \text{ kg m/s} = 2 \text{ kg} \times ?$

So the velocity of the second ball must be 3 m/s, in the same direction.

10 a A car of mass 1000 kg with a velocity of 25 m/s hits a bus of mass 10 000 kg. Assuming all the momentum is passed to the bus, how fast does the bus travel after the collision?

b A tennis racket of mass 1 kg with a velocity of 20 m/s hits a tennis ball of mass 0.1 kg. If the ball leaves the racket at 40 m/s, then calculate:

i) the momentum of the tennis racket before the collision

ii) the momentum of the ball after the collision

iii) the momentum the racket still has after the collision

iv) the velocity of the racket after the collision.

11 A hockey stick of mass 1.5 kg hits a hockey ball of mass
0.25 kg. After the collision the ball moves with a velocity of
30 m/s and the hockey stick stops. What was the speed of
the hockey stick before the collision?

More about momentum

Another way of stating the law of conservation of momentum is that
the total momentum of a closed system cannot change. A closed
system is simply one to which nothing is added or taken away. It
could be a pair of snooker balls, the Earth, or the whole universe.
Momentum is a vector quantity. Thus, an object moving in one
direction has the negative of the amount of momentum that an
identical object has moving in the opposite direction.

If we throw a 1 kg brick vertically upwards at 10 m/s, the brick has a
momentum, p, given by

$p = mv$

$p = 1 \text{ kg} \times 10 \text{ m/s}$

$p = 10 \text{ kg m/s}$

The system of the brick and the Earth originally had no momentum
so where has this momentum come from?

The answer is that the Earth has moved off in the opposite direction
with an equal and opposite momentum, so that the total momentum
of the Earth plus ball system is zero, as it was before we threw the
ball.

How fast does the Earth move as a result? The Earth's momentum
must also be 10 kg m/s in the opposite direction. The mass of the
Earth is 1×10^{24} kg. Hence,

$10 \text{ kg m/s} = 1 \times 10^{24} \text{ kg} \times v$

So the velocity of the Earth is 1×10^{-23} m/s in the opposite direction
to that in which the ball was thrown. At this velocity it would take
the earth over 300 000 years to cover a distance equal to the width of
an atom! (an atom is about 1.0×10^{-10} m in diameter). No wonder we
do not notice this movement!

12 All 5×10^9 people on the Earth gather on the Isle of Man. At
an agreed time they all jump up so their maximum upward
velocity is 20 m/s. The average mass of each person is
60 kg. If the Earth has a mass of 1×10^{24} kg, how fast does it
move downwards?

13 A gun is used to fire a 0.01 kg bullet at 1000 m/s.

   a The gun has a mass of 2 kg. How fast is it propelled
   backwards?

   b If the individual firing the gun has a mass of 78 kg, how
   fast is he or she propelled backwards?

14 In some films, actors are seen being thrown backwards by the impact of a bullet. Yet the person firing the gun is unaffected. Explain why this is not possible.

Force and acceleration

We saw at the beginning of the chapter that a force has the effect of changing the motion of an object. More precisely, an unbalanced force acting on an object makes it accelerate. The greater the force, the greater the acceleration. The greater the mass, the smaller the acceleration. This is summed up in the following equation:

$$a = \frac{F}{m}$$

This is more often written as

$$F = ma$$

where   F is the unbalanced force acting on the object in newtons (N)
       m is its mass in kg
       a is the acceleration in m/s/s

It is important to realise that F represents the *unbalanced* force on the object. An object may have several forces on it – only the unbalanced or resultant force causes it to accelerate. You will have at least two forces acting on you at the moment – gravity pulling you down and your chair pushing you upwards. These are of the same size and in opposite directions so they cancel. There is no unbalanced force so you do not accelerate.

A 1000 kg car, travelling along a straight track, accelerates from rest to 25 m/s in 10 s. What is the unbalanced force on the car?

$$a = \frac{v - u}{t}$$

$$a = \frac{(25 - 0)\ \text{m/s}}{10\ \text{s}} = 2.5\ \text{m/s/s}$$

$$F = ma$$

$$F = 1000\ \text{kg} \times 2.5\ \text{m/s/s} \quad = 2500\ \text{N}$$

In questions 15 to 19, assume travel is in a straight line.

15 A cyclist accelerates from rest to 6 m/s in 2 s. Her mass (including the cycle) is 60 kg. With what force is she pushing herself forward?

16 An Intercity 125 train accelerates from rest to 40 m/s in 40 s. The train has a mass of 200 000 kg. What is the accelerating force?

17 A force of 2000 N is used to slow down a 1000 kg car from 30 m/s to a stop. What is its acceleration? How long will it take to stop?

18 An aircraft of mass 20 000 kg accelerates at 11 m/s/s. What is the unbalanced force?

19 An electron inside your television set accelerates from rest to 3×10^7 m/s in a time of 1×10^{-9} s . If the mass of an electron is 6×10^{-31} kg, what is the accelerating force on the electron?

Combining equations of motion in a straight line

So far we have seen several different equations to describe the movements of objects travelling in a straight line. It is possible to combine two or more of these equations to make them more convenient to use. We shall use the symbols:

v = final velocity   s = distance travelled   a = steady acceleration
u = initial velocity   t = time taken

If an object accelerates with constant acceleration, a, in a straight line, then its velocity increases by an amount, a, every second, so that after t seconds its velocity has increased by an amount a × t. If it started with a velocity u, its final velocity will be u + a × t. This is the first equation of motion

v = u + at   ... (1)

Now suppose that, instead of knowing that the object accelerated for a *time*, t, we know that the object accelerated over a *distance*, s. What is the equation for its final velocity? The equation connecting s with the average velocity is

$$\text{average velocity} \quad = \quad \frac{s}{t} = \frac{u + v}{2}$$

so the time taken, t, is t = 2s/(u + v).

Replacing t in the equation (1) with this expression gives

v = u + 2as/(u + v)

Multiplying this out gives us

v(u + v) = u(u + v) + 2as

or $vu + v^2 = u^2 + uv + 2as$

which gives us the second equation of motion:

$v^2 = u^2 + 2as$ ... (2)

Finally, if an object started with velocity u, and accelerated for time t, how far did it travel? Here we can use equation (1) together with the definition of average velocity:

$$v = u + at \quad \text{and} \quad \text{average velocity} \quad = \frac{s}{t} \quad = \frac{u + v}{2}$$

So,
$$s \quad = \frac{(u + v)t}{2}$$

Since v = u + at,
$$s \quad = \frac{(u + u + at)t}{2}$$

$$s \quad = \frac{(2u + at)t}{2}$$

and this gives us the last equation of motion:

$s = ut + \frac{1}{2}at^2$ ... (3)

Use the above equations of motion to tackle the following questions.

20 A ball is dropped from a height of 16 m. If the ball starts from rest, how long does it take to hit the ground? (Assume it accelerates at 10 m/s/s.)

21 A motorbike accelerates to a speed of 12 m/s, starting from rest, over a distance of 36 m. If the bike has a mass of 250 kg, what force is provided by the engine?

22 A parachutist freefalls for 7 s. If he leaves the plane from rest, how fast is he going at the end of his free fall (assume he accelerates at 10 m/s)? Do you think the assumption is a reasonable one?

Answers

1 Vectors: electric current, force

2 a 0; b 300 N to the right; c 50 000 N upwards

3 a 0.5 km per minute due South
  b 10 metres per second   c 1000 miles per hour

4 a 0.5 km per minute

  b stage 1:   0.8 km per minute approximately NE
    stage 2:   0.5 km per minute approximately N
    stage 3:   0.6 km per minute approximately W
    stage 4:   0.3 km per minute approximately S

  c stage 4

5 a 5 m/s b 325 m/s c 25 m/s; 750 m

6 a i 1 m/s/s ii 1.25 m/s/s iii 1.67 m/s/s
    iv 3.13 m/s/s v 8.33 m/s/s

  b 3 m/s/s

  c The cyclist will not be able to keep pedalling at that rate of power output.

  d 93 m/s

7 a 30 m/s b 15 m/s c 45 m

8 30 m/s; 300 m

9 a 700 kg m/s b 12 m/s c 80 kg d 8 kg m/s
  e 20 000 000 kg m/s

10 a 2.5 m/s
   b i 20 kg m/s ii 4 kg m/s
     iii 16 kg m/s iv 16 kg m/s

11 5 m/s

12 6×10^{-12} m/s

13 a 5 m/s b 0.125 m/s   (Note: the individual also carries the gun.)

14 The momentum of the gun, bullet and firer is zero before firing. As the bullet is fired forward, the firer must move backwards with an equal and opposite amount of momentum to that of the bullet. The bullet's momentum will eventually be transferred to the victim who will therefore be thrown back as hard as the firer is thrown back.

15 180 N

16 200 000 N

17 2 m/s/s (in the direction opposite to its direction of travel); 15 s

18 220 000 N

19 1.8×10^{-14} N

20 1.8 s

21 500 N

22 70 m/s. No. Air resistance would reduce his acceleration.

Chapter 4

Current electricity

Do you understand the following terms:
conductor, insulator, electron, electric circuit, series circuit, parallel circuit? Write a sentence or two (no more) to explain what you mean by each term, then check in the glossary.

You should know these circuit symbols:

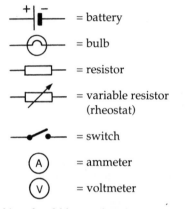

—+⊣|⊢− = battery

—⊖— = bulb

—▭— = resistor

—◿— = variable resistor (rheostat)

—•⁄— = switch

Ⓐ = ammeter

Ⓥ = voltmeter

You should know that there are two types of electric charge – positive and negative. Like charges repel and unlike charges attract.

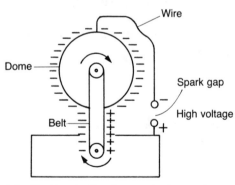

4.1   The Van de Graaff generator 'pumps' charge on to its dome.

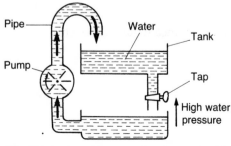

4.2   This tank and pump system is comparable with a Van de Graaff generator.

A mental picture of electricity

Electrical effects are caused by minute negatively charged particles called electrons that cannot be seen and which interact through an invisible force. Fortunately, we can often compare electricity to something that we are more familiar with – the behaviour of water as it flows through pipes. Scientists often use mental models like this to help them understand things but they have to be aware that such comparisons are not always exact.

Static electricity

Static electricity is what makes dry hair crackle when you comb it and it is what attracts small pieces of paper to a plastic ruler after it has been rubbed with a dry cloth. We can produce a larger quantity of static electricity with a Van de Graaff generator (see Fig 4.1). This machine has a rubber belt, rather like a conveyer belt, which carries electric charge on to its dome. There is an analogy between a Van de Graaff generator and the water pump and tank shown in Fig 4.2.

The volume of water stored in the tank is analogous to the electric charge stored by the dome of the Van de Graaff generator. Electric charge is simply a measurement of a quantity of electrons and is measured in **coulombs**. It compares to a quantity of water measured in gallons. One coulomb consists of about 6×10^{18} electrons, so each electron has charge of about 1.6×10^{-19} coulombs.

Pumping the water into the tank builds up a pressure. The electrical equivalent of this is the potential, measured in volts, and sometimes loosely called 'voltage'. Thus we can now visualise why sparks fly off the dome of the Van de Graaff. The potential difference between the dome and the surroundings builds up as more and more electrons are pushed on to the dome. Eventually this becomes high enough to break down the insulation of the air and cause electrons to flow out of the dome as a spark. This is similar to the pressure of the water inside the tank in Fig 4.2 becoming so great that a pressure relief valve on the tank opens and water escapes.

Current electricity

Here, too, you may find the analogy between the flow of electric charge and flow of water helpful, see Fig 4.3.

The battery drives electrons around the circuit and through a component which resists the flow. It is comparable to a pump driving water through pipework which includes a narrow section.

An ammeter measures the rate at which charge flows through the circuit. It corresponds to a water flowmeter.

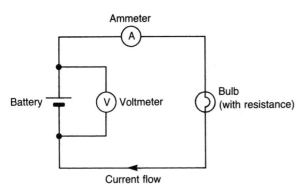

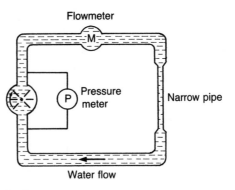

A voltmeter measures the difference in electrical potential (potential difference) between two points in the circuit – in this case either side of the battery. This is like a water pressure meter.

4.3 There is an analogy between the electric circuit and the water circuit.

Electric current

Electric current (symbol I) is the rate of flow of electric charge (symbol Q). It is measured in coulombs (symbol C) per second or amperes – usually shortened to amps (symbol A). One amp is a flow of charge of one coulomb per second. Hence,

$$I = \frac{Q}{t}$$

where   I is current in amps
           Q is charge in coulombs
           t is time in seconds

So a current of 1 amp is flowing along a wire if 1 coulomb (6×10^{18} electrons) flows through that wire every second.

1 A current of two amps flows through a light bulb. How much charge flows through the light bulb in 30 seconds?
2 The charge flowing from a battery every five seconds is 10 C. What current is flowing?

Currents around a circuit

Electric charge is not used up when it flows around a circuit. In a circuit like the one in Fig 4.3, we will get the same value for the current wherever we put the ammeter. This is because there is only one possible path for the charge to take, and none of it can escape.

In a circuit like the one in Fig 4.4, however, there are three paths for the current. When the current gets to point P, it must split into three. However, as no current can escape, the sum of the currents flowing in each branch must be equal to the original current. Or, expressed mathematically, where I_t is the total current,

4.4 Adding currents.

$$I_t = I_1 + I_2 + I_3$$

3 Work out the missing ammeter readings in Figs 4.5 to 4.7.

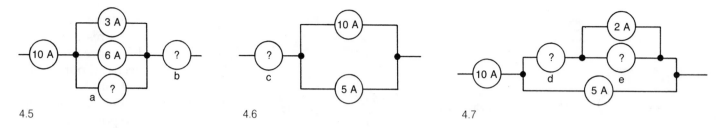

4.5   4.6   4.7

Potential difference

An electric current will flow around a circuit if there is a difference in electrical potential between two points in it. This is rather like saying that water will flow if there is a height difference between two points on the ground. The water will flow from high to low. Electric charge will flow from a high electrical potential to a low one. Electric potential measures the amount of energy that a charge has at any point. So charge will flow from a high energy point to a lower one if it is free to move. It is the **potential difference** (symbol V) between the two points which matters. This is often loosely called the voltage since it is measured in volts.

Definition of the volt

The potential difference between two points is 1 volt if 1 joule of energy is transformed when 1 coulomb of charge is moved between the two points. So,

1 volt = 1 joule/coulomb

This is a very important statement indeed. It tells us that there will be an energy change of 1 joule for every coulomb that moves through a potential difference of 1 volt. Expressed mathematically, the energy change, W, of a charge, Q, as it moves through a potential difference of V volts is given by,

$W = QV$

If we have a positive charge and it moves from positive to negative, it will move of its own accord and *give up* energy. If it moves from negative to positive, it will have to be pushed by some external force and it will *gain* energy.

An electric heater is switched on for one minute. Fifteen coulombs of charge moves through a potential difference of 240 V. How much heat energy is produced?

$W = QV$

$W = 15\,\text{C} \times 240\,\text{V} = 3600\,\text{J}$

Heat energy produced = 3600 J

4 How much energy is transformed if:
   a 1 C moves through a potential difference of 10 V?
   b 12 C moves through a potential difference of 2 V?
   c 1 electron moves through a potential difference of 10 V?

The television tube

A television screen emits light energy due to speeding electrons hitting the phosphor particles coating the face of the tube (Fig 4.8). The energy transformed into light comes from the kinetic energy of the electrons. The electrons produced by the electron gun are accelerated towards the screen due to the attraction of the high positive potential there. The greater the potential, the greater the acceleration, and the higher the final velocity and kinetic energy the electrons have as they hit the screen.

The tube designer needs a way to determine what potential difference is required between the electron and the screen to give electrons the levels of kinetic energy needed for normal operation of a TV tube.

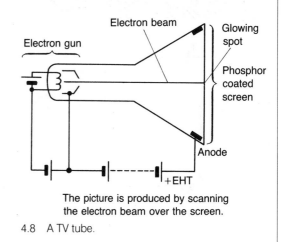

The picture is produced by scanning the electron beam over the screen.

4.8   A TV tube.

The potential difference between the screen and the electron gun of a TV tube is 15 000 V. How much kinetic energy does each electron have as it hits the screen?

$$W = QV$$

where W = energy given to electron
  V = the potential difference across the tube
  Q = the charge of an electron

$$W = 1.6 \times 10^{-19}\ C \times 15\ 000\ V = 2.4 \times 10^{-15}\ J$$

The kinetic energy of the electron as it hits the screen is $2.4 \times 10^{-15}\ J$

5 See if you can calculate the velocity of the electron just before it hits the screen. Hint: rearrange $KE = \frac{1}{2}mv^2$, see Chapter 2. The mass of the electron is 0.9×10^{-30} kg.

Potential differences around a circuit

Potential differences between different points in a circuit add up. So in Fig 4.9, the total potential difference, $V_t = V_1 + V_2 + V_3$. This is just like saying that the heights in Fig 4.10 add up.

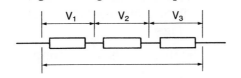

4.9   Adding potential differences.

$$V_t = V_1 + V_2 + V_3$$

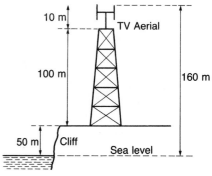

4.10   Adding heights.

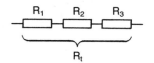

6 Work out the missing voltmeter readings in Figs 4.11 to 4.13.

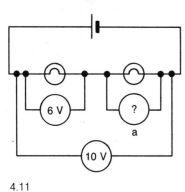

4.11

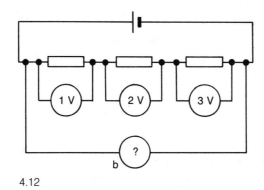

4.12

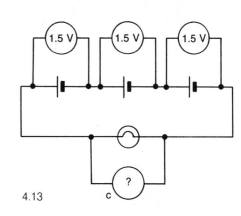

4.13

Resistance

Resistance (symbol R), measured in ohms (symbol Ω), is a measure of how difficult it is for the current to flow through a particular component (a resistor) in the circuit. The greater the resistance, the smaller the current flow (for a given potential difference). A part of a circuit with a high resistance is rather like a narrow pipe in a plumbing system which the water will find difficult to pass through.

7 Would you expect thick or thin wire (of the same metal) to have the higher resistance?

Most electric circuits have several components so it is useful to be able to calculate the overall effect that several resistors have when they are used in combination.

Resistors in series

In a series circuit, the current must all flow through each component in succession, see Fig 4.14.

The rule for combining resistances in this case is very simple. The total resistance, $R_t = R_1 + R_2 + R_3$

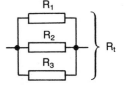

4.14   Resistors in series.

Resistors in parallel

In a parallel circuit, there are two or more alternative paths for the current which will split itself amongst the alternative branches, see Fig 4.15.

The rule here is not so simple! It is

$$\frac{1}{R_t} = \frac{1}{R_1} + \frac{1}{R_2} + \frac{1}{R_3}$$

4.15   Resistors in parallel.

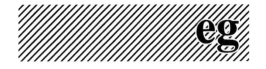

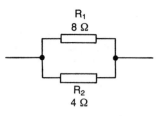

4.16   Resistors in parallel.

What is the total resistance of the combination of resistors in Fig 4.16?

$$\frac{1}{R_t} = \frac{1}{R_1} + \frac{1}{R_2}$$

$1/R_t = 1/(8 \ \Omega) + 1/(4 \ \Omega)$

$1/R_t = 1/(8 \ \Omega) + 2/(8 \ \Omega) = 3/(8 \ \Omega)$

$R_t = 8 \ \Omega/3 = 2.67 \ \Omega$

Notice that in a parallel circuit the total resistance is *less* than the smaller of the separate resistances. This is because the provision of an extra path must make it easier for the current to flow.

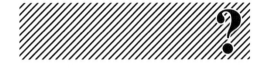

8   Find the total resistance of the combinations of resistors shown in Figs 4.17 to 4.19.

a

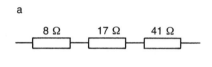

| 8 Ω | 17 Ω | 41 Ω |

4.17

b

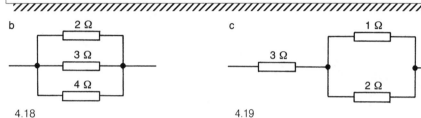

2 Ω
3 Ω
4 Ω

4.18

c

1 Ω
3 Ω
2 Ω

4.19

Ammeters

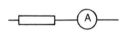

4.20   Ammeters are connected in series.

Ammeters measure electric current. The current must pass through them if they are to be able to measure it. Therefore ammeters must be connected in series with the circuit, see Fig 4.20. They must have a very low resistance so that they do not affect the current flowing.

Voltmeters

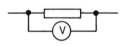

4.21   Voltmeters are connected in parallel.

Voltmeters measure potential difference between two points in the circuit. This is the energy difference which makes the current flow. Voltmeters must therefore be connected between the two points, see Fig 4.21. They must have a high resistance so that they do not allow a significant current to flow through them or they could affect the very thing we are trying to measure.

9   In Fig 4.22, where would you place a voltmeter to measure the potential difference across bulb A and an ammeter to measure the current through bulb B?

Ohm's Law

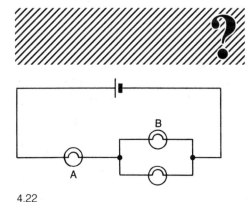

4.22

In the 1820s, Georg Ohm investigated the electrical properties of metallic materials. He found that the current through any particular piece of metal (which we shall call a resistor) was always

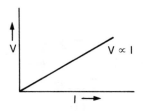

4.23   Ohm's Law.

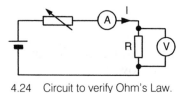

4.24   Circuit to verify Ohm's Law.

The equation can be rearranged as   V = RI.
You can remember this with the phrase 'the
Vicar is a **R**eligious **I**nstructor'.

Table 4.1   Current through, and potential
difference across, a length of wire.

Potential difference, V, in volts	Current, I, in amps	V/I
1	0.1	
2	0.2	
3	0.3	
4	0.4	
5	0.5	

proportional to the potential difference across it, provided the
temperature remained constant, see Figs 4.23 and 4.24.

Expressed mathematically,

$$I \propto V$$

where   V is the potential difference across a resistor
            I is the current through the resistor

An alternative way of expressing the same thing is that, for a
particular resistor, V/I is always a constant number. We call this
constant R, the resistance of this resistor. In general,

$$R = \frac{V}{I} \quad \text{where R is the resistance in ohms } (\Omega)$$

This equation can be used to calculate the resistance of any device.

A resistor has a resistance of 1 Ω if a current of 1 A flows through it
when there is a potential difference of 1 V across it.

10 Table 4.1 gives values of current through and voltage
     across a length of wire, obtained using a circuit such as that
     in Fig 4.24.
     a For each pair of readings, work out V/I. Is it constant?
     b What is the resistance of the piece of wire in Ω?

11 What is the resistance of a bulb if the current through it is
     2 A and the potential difference across it is 4 V?

12 What is the current flowing through a 5 Ω resistor if the
     potential difference across it is
     20 V?

13 Two bulbs are connected in series
     as shown in Fig 4.25.
     a What is the total resistance of the
        two bulbs?
     b Now calculate the current
        flowing through the circuit.

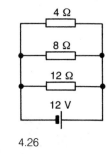

4.25

14 Three resistors are connected in parallel
     as shown in Fig 4.26.
     a What is the total resistance of the
        resistors?
     b Now calculate the current taken from
        the 12 V supply.

15 A bulb has a resistance of 5 ohms
     in Fig 4.27. Calculate the value of
     the series resistance to limit the
     current to 0.2 amps from the 10
     V supply.

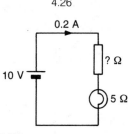

4.27

Power

Power is the rate of transforming energy from one form to another (see Chapter 2). Power is usually measured in joules per second, or watts (symbol W).

$$\text{Power (watts)} = \frac{\text{Energy (joules)}}{\text{Time (seconds)}}$$

The 60 W bulb by which you may be reading this book is transforming 60 J of electrical energy into 60 J of heat and light energy every second.

16 A 40 W bulb is switched on for 60 seconds. How much energy does it transform?

Electrical Power

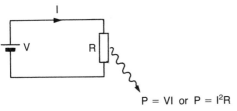

$P = VI$ or $P = I^2R$

4.28   Power dissipated by a resistor.

Whenever an electric current flows through a part of a circuit, some of the electrical energy is transformed into heat, see Fig 4.28. The rate of transformation of energy depends on the current flowing through the wire and the potential difference across it.

If there is a current of 2 A, two coulombs pass through the resistor each second. If there is a potential difference of 10 V, each coulomb gives up 10 J of energy as it passes through. So each second, $2 \times 10\,\text{J} = 20\,\text{J}$ is converted from electrical energy to heat. In general,

$$\text{Power} = \text{potential difference} \times \text{current}$$
$$P = VI$$

Most electrical domestic equipment is marked only with its power rating, so how do you calculate its current consumption to allow you to choose the correct fuse?

An electric kettle has a power rating of 2000 W and operates from the 240 V mains. Which of the following fuses would you use: 1, 2, 3, 5, 7, 10, 13 A?

$$P = VI \quad \text{or} \quad I = \frac{P}{V} = \frac{2000\,\text{W}}{240\,\text{V}} = 8.3\,\text{A}$$

You must use a fuse a bit larger than this – a 10 amp fuse.

17 What is the power of a 12 V bulb which has a current of 1 A flowing through it?

> 18 A car headlamp bulb has a power rating of 60 W. It runs
>   from a 12 V battery. What is the current flowing through it?
>   Given the range of fuses in the previous example, what size
>   fuse would you use?

Calculating power developed in resistances

There is an important variant of P = VI.

$$P = VI \qquad \dots (1)$$
$$V = RI \qquad \dots (2) \qquad \text{This is 'Ohm's Law'}$$

Substitute (2) into (1)

$$P = I^2R$$

This tells us that the power developed in a resistance is proportional
to the square of the current. It has many important implications – see
the following.

The national grid

The national grid, see Fig 4.29, is the system which distributes electrical energy from power stations to homes,
schools, factories and so on. It operates by using transformers (see Chapter 5) to step up the voltage to about
300 kV (300 000 V) and then step it down again to 240 V. Why?

The reason is to minimise the loss of power caused by heat generated in the power lines. Imagine we have to
supply 10 kW (10 000 W) of power (enough to run ten electric bar heaters) through power lines of resistance 1 Ω.

We know that   P = VI
               P = 10 000 W
so, $V \times I = 10\ 000$ W

Case 1   We could choose to supply this power at 100 000 V. Substituting into the equation above,

$$100\ 000\ \text{V} \times I = 10\ 000\ \text{W}$$
$$I = 0.1\ \text{A}$$

The power loss (as heat) is given by   P = I²R   so the rate of heat loss will be   0.1 A × 0.1 A × 1 Ω = 0.01 W

That is, 0.01/10 000 of the power being supplied (0.0001%) is wasted heating up the power lines.

Case 2   We could choose to supply this power at 200 V, in which case the current, I, woud be 50 A. Check that
this is correct by a calculation like the one above.

The rate of heat loss is given by   P = I²R   so the rate of heat loss will be   50 A × 50 A × 1 Ω = 2500 W

That is, 2500/10 000 of the power being supplied (25 %) is wasted heating up the power lines.

The choice between these two alternatives is not difficult!

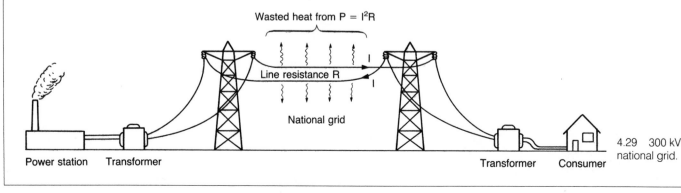

4.29   300 kV
national grid.

Electrical energy

We have seen that the power, P, generated by an electric current is given by:

$$P = VI$$

This is the energy transformed per second. If the current flows for a time t seconds, the total energy transformed, W, will be given by:

$$W = VIt$$

19 A 3000 watt kettle is switched on for 2 minutes. How much energy has it transformed?

Answers

1 60 C

2 2 A

3 a 1 A   b 10 A   c 15 A   d 5 A   e 3 A

4 a 10 J   b 24 J   c 1.6×10^{-18} J

5 7.3×10^7 m/s   ($\frac{1}{4}$ of the speed of light!)

6 a 4 V   b 6 V   c 4.5 V

7 Thin wire.

8 a 66 Ω   b 0.92 Ω   c 3.67 Ω

9 Voltmeter, across A, that is, in a parallel circuit across A. Ammeter, next to B, between B and the circuit junction.

10 a All the ratios of V/I are the same, with a value of 10.

   b 10 Ω

11 2 Ω

12 4 A

13 a 10 Ω   b 1.5 A

14 a 2.18 Ω   b 5.5 A

15 45 Ω

16 2400 J

17 12 W

18 5 A;   7 A

19 360 000 J

Chapter 5   Electromagnetism

Do you understand the following terms: **direct current, alternating current**? Write a sentence or two (no more) to explain what you understand by each term, then check in the glossary.

Using electromagnetism

Did you know all the following devices (and many more) operate by electromagnetism?

- electric motors
- microphones
- loudspeakers
- electric bells and buzzers
- disc drives
- video recorders

The key to the operation of electromagnetic devices is the fact that a magnetic field is produced when an electric current flows.

1 Write down at least three important facts about how magnets behave.

2 Draw the shape of the magnetic field around a bar magnet.

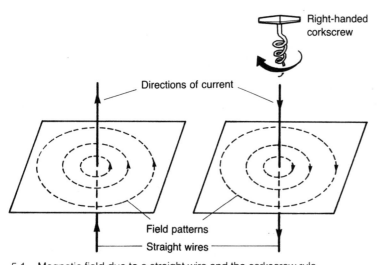

5.1   Magnetic field due to a straight wire and the corkscrew rule.

The magnetic effect of an electric current

The term 'field' describes how magnetic force reaches out through space. So magnets can attract and repel without touching. Magnetic fields are drawn as lines – the closer the lines, the stronger the field. These lines have arrows drawn on them which indicate the direction in which the North pole of a small magnet would point when placed in the field. Thus the field lines are shown going from north to south.

If a current flows along a straight wire, a circular magnetic field is produced, as shown in Fig 5.1. The direction of the field can be found by the 'corkscrew rule', as shown.

3 Draw the field produced by the current flowing in Fig 5.2. Show its direction.

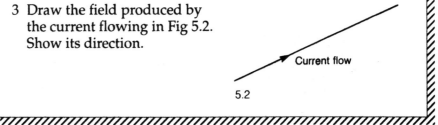

Permanent magnets

Many people believe that permanent magnetism and electromagnetism are quite different. In fact they are due to exactly the same thing – the movement of charge. At the atomic level, negatively charged electrons 'spin' as they 'orbit' the nucleus. This spin makes each electron into a tiny electromagnet and if enough spins line up, the magnetism becomes strong enough to be noticed. Iron in particular shows this strongly, but other elements are magnetic to a lesser extent.

The magnetism of planets such as the Earth must also be due to the movement of charge, and it is thought that this may be due to the flow of ionised particles in currents in the molten interior of the Earth caused by its rotation.

The pole of a magnet that points to the geographical North of the Earth is called the North pole of that magnet. It is attracted to the South pole of other magnets. So the geographical North pole of the Earth is really the South pole of the Earth's magnetic field!

Concentrating magnetic fields

Compared with a straight wire, a single turn of wire increases the magnetic field, as shown in Fig 5.3.

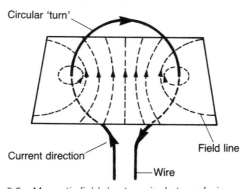

5.3   Magnetic field due to a single turn of wire.

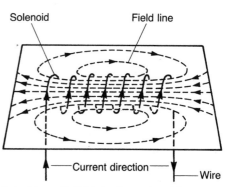

5.4   Magnetic field due to a solenoid.

4 Use the corkscrew rule to check that the direction of the current in the turn of wire in Fig 5.3 has been given correctly.

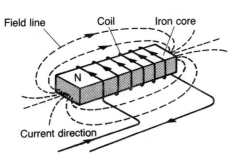

5.5   Electromagnet with an iron core.

A solenoid (a long coil of wire, as shown in Fig 5.4) increases the field further still, as all the individual turns contribute to the overall field strength.

Placing an iron core in the solenoid (Fig 5.5) increases the magnetic field still more, to make an even stronger magnet. This is because magnetic materials such as iron enhance magnetic fields.

The strongest magnets have their poles placed close together as in the electromagnet with an iron 'C' core (so called for its shape) shown in Fig 5.6. This is because the field has to pass through only a small distance of air.

The iron cores in Figs 5.5 and 5.6 become magnets while the current is flowing. The North pole is marked on Fig 5.5.

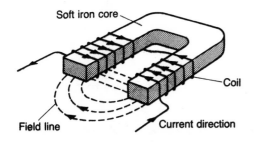

5.6   Electromagnet with an iron 'C' core.

5 Use the direction of the field lines to find which pole is North in Fig 5.6.

6 Give an application of electromagnets. Why are they more useful than permanent magnets?

The electric motor effect

In the electric motor, electrical energy is converted into kinetic (moving) energy. We know that one magnetic field interacts with another to produce a force (unlike poles attract and like poles repel). So a current-carrying wire has a force exerted on it by a magnetic field. This may cause it to move, as shown in Fig 5.7.

The 'catapult' effect

Fig 5.8a shows the separate fields produced by the wire and the magnet. Fig 5.8b shows the resulting combined field. Note, here, how the field is concentrated on one side of the wire and weakened on the other. The result is that the wire appears to be in a 'catapult' which propels it at right angles to the magnet's field.

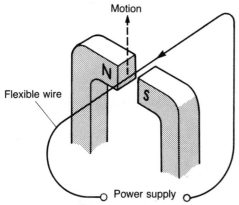

5.7   Current-carrying wire in a strong magnetic field.

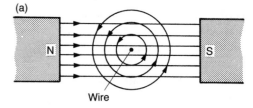

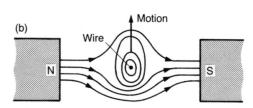

5.8   The catapult effect.

Although it is the wire that we see moving, it is really the electrons inside the wire that have the force exerted on them.

7 Mark on a copy of Fig 5.8b where the field is strongest and where it is weakest. Does the wire move from strong field to weak or from weak to strong?

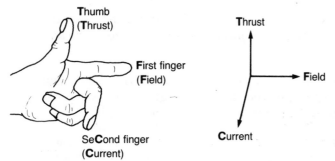

Fleming's left-hand (or motor) rule

We can work out the direction that a wire in a magnetic field will move by Fleming's left-hand (or motor) rule, as shown in Fig 5.9.

5.9   Fleming's left-hand (or motor) rule.

8 Work out the direction that the wires in Figs 5.10, a to c, would move.

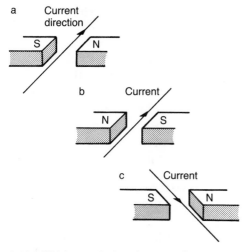

5.10   Which way do the wires move?

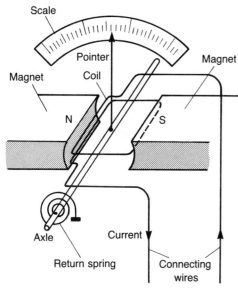

5.12   DC meter.

Direct current (DC) electric motor

If a wire can be moved by a magnetic field, it is a simple engineering problem to harness this movement usefully. Fig 5.11 shows a simple electric motor. The current flowing through the coil in the magnetic field creates a force on each side of the coil in the directions shown. The directions of these forces can be predicted using Fleming's left-hand rule. Check that you get the same directions as those shown by the arrows in Fig 5.11. As these forces are in opposite directions, they tend to make the coil rotate as shown. The electric current flows from the external circuit into the coil via carbon brushes which rest gently on the commutator. The commutator rotates with the coil so that the current always flows in the same direction around it.

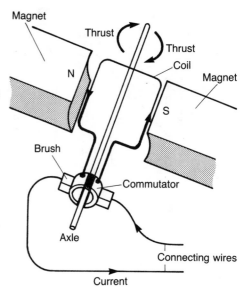

5.11   DC electric motor.

Direct current (DC) meter

The DC meter works on the same principle as the electric motor except that the coil turns against a spring and there is no need for a commutator. A simplified diagram of such a meter is shown in Fig 5.12. When a current flows through the coil, the coil twists in just the same way as it does in a motor. However, as it twists, it tightens up the coiled spring until the twisting force due to the current equals the opposing force due to the spring. So the bigger the current, the bigger the deflection of the meter. This is the basis of both ammeters and voltmeters.

9 Suggest three ways of increasing the force which makes the DC electric motor work.

10 a Explain why the DC meter needs no commutator.

    b How could we make the DC meter more sensitive – that is get a bigger movement from the same current?

The electric effect of magnetism

We have seen how electricity creates magnetism. Now we will look at how magnetism can create electricity. This is known as **electromagnetic induction** and was discovered by Michael Faraday in 1831. It is the basis of all electrical generators. These convert kinetic energy into electrical energy.

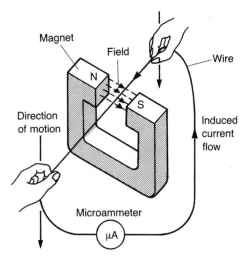

5.13   Current is induced in a wire moving in a magnetic field.

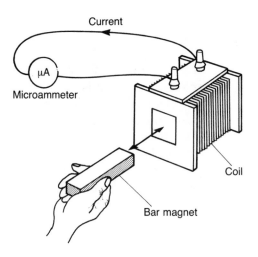

5.14   Current is induced in a coil by a changing magnetic field.

Electromagnetic induction

If a wire is moved through a strong magnetic field, as shown in Fig 5.13, the electrons are pushed to one side and flow along the wire as current. This induced current flows only whilst the wire is in motion.

A current is also induced if the magnet moves and the wire is still, see Fig 5.14. The important point is that only relative movement is needed.

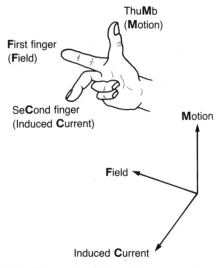

5.15   Fleming's right-hand (dynamo) rule.

If you have difficulty recalling which hand to use for which of Fleming's rules, remember that *motors* drive on the *left*.

Faraday's law of electromagnetic induction

If no circuit is connected across the coil in Fig 5.14, the electrons will build up at the end of the wire to create a potential difference across it. This potential difference is known as an **electromotive force**, or emf for short. This is the potential difference which would make the current flow if there were a circuit. Faraday found that the emf depended on three things:

- the relative speeds of the magnet and coil
- the number of turns of the coil
- the strength of the magnetic field

Faraday's law of electromagnetic induction states that the induced emf is proportional to each of the factors above.

Fleming's right-hand (dynamo) rule

The direction of the induced current can be determined by Fleming's right-hand (dynamo) rule, as shown in Fig 5.15.

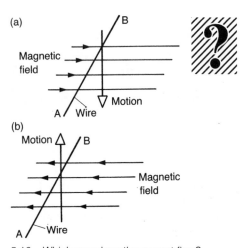

5.16   Which way does the current flow?

> 11 Work out the direction of the induced current in Figs 5.16 a and b.

Direct current (DC) generator (dynamo)

Currents induced by wires moving in magnetic fields are the basis of electric generators, from bicycle dynamos to those used by the electricity supply industry.

If we consider the system for the DC electric motor (see Fig 5.11), but instead of supplying current, we supply drive to the axle, we can see that an emf will be induced and thus current will flow.

You can convince yourself that motors can work as generators as follows. Connect a milli-ammeter across the terminals of a small DC motor, such as is found in some toys, and spin the axle. You will see a small current registered.

Alternating current (AC) generator

This is of even greater importance than the DC generator since mains electricity is AC so that it can be transformed up and down efficiently. See Chapter 4, The national grid.

The only basic difference from the DC generator is that slip rings are used instead of a commutator, see Fig 5.17. As the coil rotates, the windings move alternately up through the magnetic field and then down again. This means that the induced current flows first in one direction and then in the other. The output current changes direction (or alternates) at the frequency of the rotational speed of the generator, which is 50 times per second (50 Hz) in the case of British mains supplies.

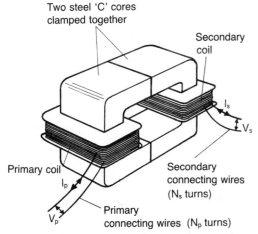

5.17   AC generator.

Transformers

Transformers are devices that can 'transform' a low potential difference up to a high potential difference and vice versa. They work only with AC supplies and are immensely important in the efficient transmission of electrical energy in the national grid (see Chapter 4), where they transform the potential difference up for transmission, and then down again for use. Transformers are also used to produce low, and therefore safe, potential differences for such as electric model trains, cassette players and radios.

The construction of a transformer is shown in Fig 5.18. Its operation is another example of electromagnetic induction. An alternating current (AC) is applied to the **primary coil** producing an alternating magnetic field in the iron core. This alternating magnetic field cuts the **secondary coil**, thus inducing an emf across it.

The following relationship applies to transformers:

$$\frac{V_s}{V_p} = \frac{N_s}{N_p}$$

where

V_p = potential difference applied across the primary coil
V_s = potential difference developed across the secondary coil
N_p = number of turns in the primary coil
N_s = number of turns in the secondary coil

5.18   The physical construction of a transformer.

This means that if we want to step up our potential difference, we must have more turns on the secondary coil than on the primary. It is the *ratio* of the number of turns on the secondary coil to the number of turns on the primary which determines by how much the transformer steps potential difference up or down. This is sometimes called the turns ratio.

A transformer has a primary coil with 2000 turns and a secondary coil with 100 turns. A potential difference of 240 V is applied across the primary. What will be the output potential difference of the secondary?

$$\frac{V_s}{V_P} = \frac{N_s}{N_P} \quad \text{so} \quad V_s = \frac{N_s \times V_P}{N_P} = \frac{100 \times 240 \text{ V}}{2000} = 12 \text{ V}$$

The output potential difference is 12 V

13 What turns ratio would you need to transform 10 kV (the output potential difference of a power station) up to 300 kV (the potential difference at which the national grid transmits electrical energy)?

Transforming the current

At first sight it looks as though we are getting something for nothing from a step up transformer. However, if we step up the potential difference, we step down the current proportionately. If no energy is lost in a transformer, the power input (to the primary) will be the same as the power output (from the secondary).

Since electrical power, $P = VI$ (see Chapter 4)

$$V_P \times I_P = V_s \times I_s$$

where
  I_P = current flowing in the primary coil
  I_s = current flowing in the secondary coil

A transformer has a primary coil of 2000 turns and a secondary coil of 100 turns. This, as we have seen in the above example, will step down a primary potential difference of 240 V to 12 V. If the current flowing in the primary coil is 0.1 A, what current will flow in the secondary?

If no energy is lost,

$$V_P \times I_P = V_s \times I_s$$
$$240 \text{ V} \times 0.1 \text{ A} = 12 \text{ V} \times I_s$$
$$I_s = 2 \text{ A}$$

A current of 2 A will flow in the secondary coil.

The step down transformer offers a useful way of providing large currents for arc welding, industrial electromagnets and other high-current devices.

14 A transformer transforms 240 V mains to 3 V for an arc welder.

   a If the primary coil has 800 turns, how many turns will there be on the secondary?

   b If the current in the welder is 250 A, what would be the primary current taken from the mains if no energy is lost?

Transformer efficiency

Transformers are very efficient devices.

A transformer has a potential difference of 400 V applied to its primary with a secondary potential difference of 1500 V. The secondary current supplied to the load is 2 amps. The current flowing in the primary is measured to be 8.5 amps. What is the efficiency of the transformer?

$$\text{Efficiency} = \frac{\text{power out}}{\text{power in}} \times 100\% = \frac{V_s \times I_s}{V_p \times I_p}$$

$$= \frac{1500 \text{ V} \times 2 \text{ A}}{400 \text{ V} \times 8.5 \text{ A}} \times 100\% = 88\%$$

15 What would be the primary current in the above example if the efficiency were   a 100%   b 80% ?

Answers

1 A material that shows magnetic effects is iron. A magnet has two poles, termed the 'North pole' and 'South pole'. Unlike poles attract, like poles repel.

2 The field looks exactly the same as that of the electromagnet in Fig 5.5.

3
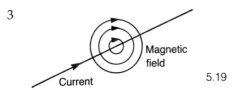
5.19

4 Yes it has.

5 The right-hand pole.

6 As just one of many examples: electromagnets can be used to pick out steel cans from aluminium cans in a recycling plant. The electromagnet can be switched off to allow the steel cans to drop into a receptacle. Electromagnets can be carefully controlled in strength, so are of use in, for example, medical applications such

as the delicate process of removing iron splinters from the eye.

7 The strongest field is where the field lines are close together – at the bottom of the diagram. The field is weakest at the top of the diagram. The wire moves from strong field to weak.

8 a up   b down   c up

9 i Increase the magnetic field.   ii Increase the number of turns on the coil.   iii Increase the current through the coil.

10 a It does not need to continually revolve.

    b i use more turns for the coil   ii use a weaker spring   iii use a stronger magnetic field

11 a B to A   b B to A

12 kinetic, electrical, electrical, kinetic

13 1 : 30

14 a 10 turns   b 3.1 A

15 a 7.5 A   b 9.4 A

Chapter 6

Vibrations and waves

Starting points

Do you understand the following terms used to describe vibrations: **frequency, time period, amplitude**? Write a sentence or two (no more) to explain what you mean by each term, then check in the glossary. You should be able to tackle question 1.

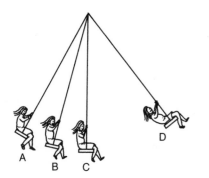

6.1 A child's swing.

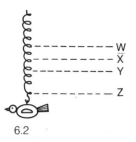

6.2

Vibrations

We often come across systems which vibrate or oscillate (the two words mean the same thing) when they are started off with a push.

Here are some examples:

*   pendulums
*   taut strings or wires, such as guitar strings
*   diving boards
*   tall buildings
*   swings
*   columns of air, such as those inside woodwind instruments

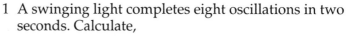

> 1 A swinging light completes eight oscillations in two seconds. Calculate,
>   a the time period,
>   b the frequency of the oscillation.

In some cases vibrations are very useful to us, as in musical instruments and pendulum clocks. Others can be dangerous. As just one instance, the Tacoma Narrows Bridge in Washington State, USA, was destroyed, in 1940, by out-of-control vibrations. It is important to understand what is going on in this kind of motion.

A very simple example to think about is a child's swing, see Fig 6.1. This is an example of a pendulum. If you look closely at this motion you will see that the speed of the swing is constantly changing. At each end of the actual oscillation, the swing itself is stationary. Its speed builds up (it accelerates) as it approaches the centre of its oscillation, where it is going fastest. One full oscillation of the swing is from A to D and back to A.

An object hung on a spring is another simple example, see Fig 6.2. If the object is pulled down so that the spring stretches and is then released, it will oscillate in an up and down motion. Again the speed will vary between zero at the extremes, W and Z, and a maximum at the central position, Y. The central position for the spring system will be the normal unstretched position.

> 2 a Using the letters shown in Figs 6.1 and 6.2, identify, for both the swing and spring systems, the positions of
>   i maximum speed   ii zero speed
>   iii a speed lower than maximum.
>   b Write down the amplitude of each of the systems.

Simple harmonic motion

Some oscillations, though not all, have a very important characteristic – they keep the same time period even though the size or amplitude of the oscillation may change. This is true in the case of both of the above examples. The pendulum clock is a further example. When the amplitude of the oscillation gets less, the maximum speed is reduced. This means that the time taken to cover the smaller distance is the same as the time to cover the original larger distance. The kind of systems which have this particular characteristic are usually called **simple harmonic oscillators**.

Forced vibrations and resonance

Oscillations tend to lose energy as they move and work against friction. The swing, for example, is working against the air and against its bearings. As an oscillation loses energy its amplitude will decrease. We can, however, prevent this by giving it a push at just the right time. The timing of the push is very important and we must also select the correct position and direction when we push a swing. If we were to choose a different timing, the response of the swing to our repeated pushes would be very poor. We can tell that our timing is right if the swing starts to build up its amplitude. This happens only when the frequency of the pushing force exactly matches the **natural frequency** of the oscillation. We call this situation **resonance**.

3 Where, when and in what direction, would you push a swing to build up its amplitude of vibration?

Resonance

There are many situations where resonance can be useful. For example, a diver from the high board builds up amplitude by jumping up and down at exactly the natural frequency of the board. Another, less obvious, example is tuning in to electrical oscillations with a radio receiver. But sometimes resonance can be dangerous. Examples include the effect of earthquakes on buildings, and regular ruts in the road which cause car bodies to oscillate. In the latter case steps must be taken to prevent the build up of amplitude. Car suspensions are designed so that oscillations will die out quite quickly: we say the oscillations are heavily **damped**. In the former case, it is important to take the natural oscillation frequency of tall buildings into account in their design.

Waves

Waves and vibrations or oscillations are often confused. This is because they are usually found together. A vibration is necessary to start a wave, and it is this vibration which is passed on to the parts of the material or **medium** that the wave travels through.

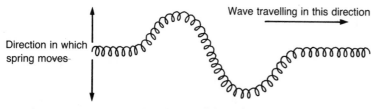

6.3   A transverse wave passing along a slinky spring.

In Fig 6.3, imagine someone at the left side of the spring, who makes one complete up and down movement or oscillation of the left-hand link in the spring. As this link moves, it pulls the next link up with it. In this way the movement made by the first link is repeated all the way along the spring. Each link, however, lags slightly behind in the oscillation compared to the link before it.

This results in the spring taking up a shape like that shown in Fig 6.3. It is this shape that we call a wave. It travels along the spring from left to right carrying with it the energy of the vibration.

There are two movements at right angles to each other in this example – the oscillation (up and down) and the moving wave (along the spring). We call this type of wave a **transverse** wave.

It is possible to send a different type of wave through the spring. The link at the left can be made to vibrate to and fro along the length of the spring. As before this will cause successive links to follow its movement, but lagging slightly behind until the vibration finally arrives at the other end. In this case the vibration and the travelling wave are both along the same line and the wave is called a **longitudinal** wave, see Fig 6.4.

6.4   A longitudinal wave passing along a slinky spring.

Waves, in general, fall into either of these two categories: transverse or longitudinal.

---

4 Suggest into which category each of these waves fits.
  a Ripples (waves) travelling across a still pond causing a toy boat to move up and down.
  b A loudspeaker causing the air to oscillate and pass a sound wave.
  c A wave produced by flicking a skipping rope.

Wave measurements

Fig 6.5 shows the side view of a transverse water wave. The wave is actually travelling, so the diagram shows its position at an instant in time (as though we had taken a snapshot of it).

Wavelength

a is the amplitude

6.5   Transverse waves.

There are two crests and two troughs shown in Fig 6.5. This means that two full oscillations have occured. The **wavelength** is the distance from any point on one wave to the same point on the next wave. For simplicity it is usually measured from crest to crest or from trough to trough. It is given the symbol λ, the Greek letter lambda.

5 If point X on Fig 6.5 is taken as the starting point for the wavelength measurement, mark the point Y where the measurement would end.

Some of the measurements made on the waves are the same as those for oscillations.

Frequency

As the waves pass along, the number of complete up and down vibrations which pass any particular point in one second is called the **frequency**. This must be the same as the number of vibrations which are made in one second at the source of the wave. We measure frequency in waves per second or cycles per second. One cycle per second is given the name hertz (Hz)

Amplitude

This is the furthest distance that the parts of the medium move from their undisturbed position. It is set by the amplitude of the oscillating source of the wave.

The wave formula

Waves often spread out in a circle from the source (think of ripples formed by dropping a stone in a pond). Sometimes, we think about a part of the wave which is moving in one particular direction, so we tend to talk about its **velocity** (see Chapter 3) rather than its speed. This is simply the distance that the wave travels in one second in a particular direction.

The velocity, v, is measured in metres per second (m/s).
The wavelength, λ, is measured in metres.
The frequency, f, is measured in waves per second or hertz (Hz).

These three values can be combined into the relationship:
$$v = f\lambda$$

Let us look at where this relationship comes from. Imagine you are watching the waves pass you. For each complete vibration, the wave itself moves on by one whole wavelength, say 0.2 metres. In one second a certain number of waves moves past, say 6 waves per second. So every second, the wave must move forward by 6×0.2 metres. This means that the velocity of the wave is 6×0.2 metres per second, that is, 1.2 metres per second.

In this example, 6 waves per second is the frequency, f, and 0.2 metres is the wavelength, λ. Multiplying these together gives us the velocity of the wave, v.

The relationship $v = f\lambda$ is true for all waves. Practise using it to answer the following questions.

6 a A wave has a frequency of 2 Hz and a wavelength of 10 cm. Work out the velocity of the wave.

b Waves travel along a spring at 150 cm/s. The end of the spring is oscillated at 20 vibrations per second. Calculate the wavelength of the waves.

c Radio waves of wavelength 1515 metres (Radio 4) have a frequency of 198 000 Hz. Calculate the velocity of these waves.

d Assuming that all radio waves travel at the same speed, work out the frequency of 275 metre wavelength waves (Radio 1).

Properties of waves

There are certain properties that all waves have. These are **reflection**, **refraction**, **diffraction**, and **interference**. In fact the scientist Thomas Young suggested, in the early 19th century, that light was a wave rather than a stream of particles when he demonstrated that it was possible both to diffract light and to cause it to interfere. Scientists had been discussing the nature of light for some time.

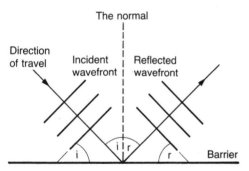

6.6   Waves hitting a barrier and being reflected.

Reflection

You are probably quite familiar with reflection. Check with the glossary that you understand the terms: **angle of incidence**, **angle of reflection**, **the normal** and the relationship between the angle of incidence, i, and the angle of reflection, r. These are shown in Fig 6.6.

Refraction

Refraction or bending occurs when a wave moves out of one substance and into another. It occurs because the wave travels at different speeds in different materials.

Fig 6.7 shows water waves in a ripple tank moving from deep to shallow water. The waves travel more slowly in the shallow region as there is more drag on them. This means that the **wavefronts** are closer together in the shallow area, so the wavelength has become smaller. As the right-hand side of the wave spends more time in the shallow region, it falls behind the left-hand side. This means that the wave is bent as it moves into the shallow region. We say the wave has been **refracted**.

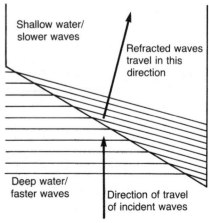

6.7   Refraction of water waves.

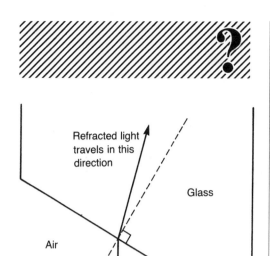

6.8 Refraction of light waves.

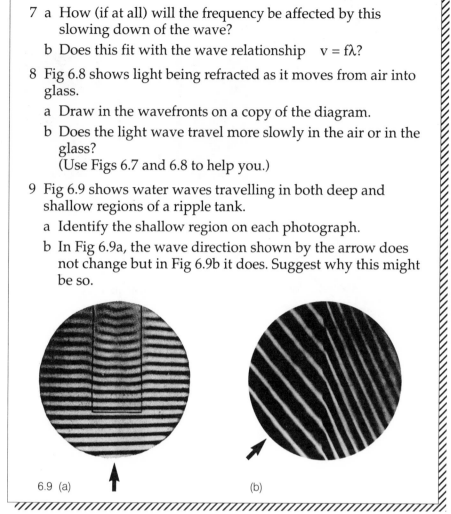

7 a How (if at all) will the frequency be affected by this slowing down of the wave?

b Does this fit with the wave relationship $v = f\lambda$?

8 Fig 6.8 shows light being refracted as it moves from air into glass.

a Draw in the wavefronts on a copy of the diagram.

b Does the light wave travel more slowly in the air or in the glass?
(Use Figs 6.7 and 6.8 to help you.)

9 Fig 6.9 shows water waves travelling in both deep and shallow regions of a ripple tank.

a Identify the shallow region on each photograph.

b In Fig 6.9a, the wave direction shown by the arrow does not change but in Fig 6.9b it does. Suggest why this might be so.

6.9 (a)   (b)

Diffraction

Diffraction is the spreading out of waves as they pass through narrow gaps. We take diffraction of sound waves for granted. We expect to be able to hear sounds from another room without having to stand opposite the door-opening. This suggests that the sound waves bend around the door-opening. We would, however, be very surprised if we could *see* the source of the sound if we were not opposite the door! Does this mean that light waves are not diffracted?

Figs 6.10a and b, which show diffraction in a ripple tank, can help us explain the difference. In each case the straight waves pass through a gap in the barrier. In Fig 6.10a, where the wavelength of the wave is about the same size as the gap, there is significant spreading out or diffraction. This is the situation with sound waves and a door-opening – sound waves are of about the same wavelength as the gap.

Fig 6.10b is more like the situation that occurs with light. The wavelength is very small compared to the size of the gap, and the diffraction effect is much less obvious.

6.10 (a)   (b)

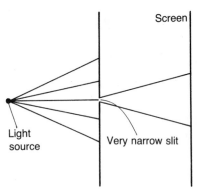

6.11   (a) Aerial view of experiment.   (b) Pattern produced at the screen.

It is possible, however, to find a gap of the correct size so that diffraction of light does occur. Fig 6.11 shows the pattern obtained on a screen when light is passed through a very narrow vertical slit (0.01 mm wide).

The middle band of the light strip is much wider than the original slit and there are further bands of light to the left and right. This shows that the light wave has spread out as it passed through the slit.

10 On the basis of the size of gap that produces diffraction, make a very rough estimate of the wavelength of
    a sound waves   b light waves.

11 Fig 6.12 shows straight waves in a ripple tank approaching a barrier. The water on the right-hand side of the barrier is much shallower than that on the left.

   a Copy Fig 6.12 and draw in the waves after they have passed through the gap.

   b Add arrows to the diagram to show the directions of the waves both before and after they go through the barrier.

6.12

Interference

6.13   Interference in a ripple tank.

This occurs when two (or more) waves meet. Each wave will affect the material or medium through which it is travelling. In water, for example, each wave may cause the water at a particular point to rise up (form a crest). The total effect will be that the water will rise by a greater amount, in fact by the sum of the heights of the individual crests. Similarly, where two troughs of the waves meet, there will be a deeper trough, equal to the sum of the two troughs. Where the crest of one wave meets the trough of the other, and they are both of the same height, they will add to produce calm water.

However, in the water we have many waves and the movements caused by each of the waves add together. We call this the **principle of superposition** and we say that the waves have interfered.

Fig 6.13 shows interference of waves in a ripple tank. S_1 and S_2 are sources of circular waves. You can see the alternate regions of still and disturbed water.

To help us to explain the appearance of the water we need to construct a diagram like the one in Fig 6.14.

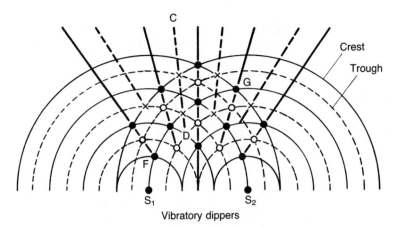

Crest

Trough

C

G

D

F

S_1 S_2
Vibratory dippers

6.14

This lets us see what effect each wave would have at every point. For example, points such as F in the diagram show where a crest from S_1 meets a crest from S_2. This will result in a high crest being produced. As another example, the line that joins C to D will have a crest meeting a trough at every point. This corresponds to a line of calm water. The overall pattern produced is called an **interference pattern** and its appearance is related to the wavelength of the waves which produce it.

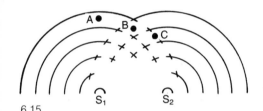

6.15

12 a Use a ruler to measure the wavelength of the waves in Fig 6.14.
 b What would you expect to see at position G?
 c Use a ruler to measure the length of a line from S_1 to position G. How many wavelengths is it?
 d Use a ruler to measure the length of a line from S_2 to position G. How many wavelengths is it?

13 Fig 6.15 shows waves spreading out from two sources, S_1 and S_2.
 a What part of the wave (crest or trough) is at A and which source is it from?
 b In the region where the waves overlap, explain how the waves will combine at positions B and C.

Electromagnetic waves

There are many different types of waves – for example water, sound, radio, gamma, and light. They all have the properties of reflection, refraction, diffraction and interference.

Some of these waves can be organised into a special group called the **electromagnetic spectrum**. They are all transverse waves which travel at a speed of three hundred million metres per second (often called the speed of light). They are able to travel through a vacuum. The reason for the name electromagnetic is that the waves all consist of oscillating electric and magnetic fields. The word spectrum indicates that the group covers a very wide range of wavelengths. The wavelengths in fact vary from as small as a million millionth of a metre for gamma rays to several kilometres for radio waves.

14 Use the wave relationship $v = f\lambda$ to work out the range of frequencies in the electromagnetic spectrum from gamma rays of wavelength 10^{-12} m to radio waves of wavelength 10^5 m. (Remember that the speed of all of these waves is the same, 3×10^8 m/s, that is, 300 000 000 m/s.)

15 Write down five properties which are common to all electromagnetic waves.

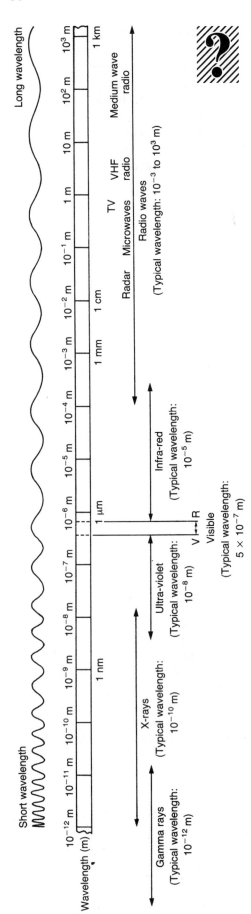

6.16   The electromagnetic spectrum.

16 In Fig 6.16 you will find the different waves which belong to the electromagnetic spectrum. Study this and then try to answer the following questions.

   a Write down a list of at least five waves which make up the electromagnetic spectrum. Place them in order of increasing wavelength.

   b State from your own reading, which waves cause a suntan. Calculate their frequency, using the typical wavelength.

   c How many times longer is the wavelength of microwaves than the typical wavelength of X-rays? From your own reading, which of them is more penetrating?

Answers

1 a 0.25 seconds   b 4 cycles per second (or hertz)

2 a swing: i C   ii A and D   iii B

   spring: i Y   ii W and Z   iii X

   b swing: distance C – D;   spring: distance Y – Z

3 The swing should be pushed at its position of maximum displacement, in a direction towards the centre of the oscillation, once every full oscillation.

4 a transverse   b longitudinal   c transverse

5 Y is in exactly the same position as X, but on the next wave.

6 a 20 cm per second

   b 7.5 cm

   c 300 million metres per second

   d 1 090 909 hertz

7 a The frequency will not be affected since the same number of waves are still being produced every second.

   b The frequency, f, is unaltered but the wavelength is reduced. This means that the velocity, v, from $v = f\lambda$ must also reduce. This fits with the relationship.

8 a See Fig 6.17.

   b It travels more slowly in glass.

9 a Inside the rectangle in photograph (a) and on the right in photograph (b).

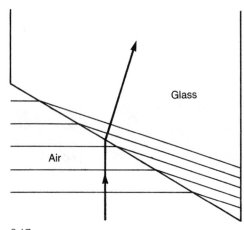

6.17

9 b In photograph (a) the whole wavefront moves on to the shallow
    region at the same time but in photograph (b) the right side of the
    wavefront is in the shallow region for a longer time than is the left.
    This means that it falls behind.

10 a A few metres

   b a few hundredths of a millimetre

11
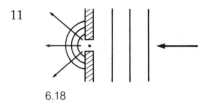

6.18

12 a 0.9 cm   b a high crest   c 4   d 3

13 a Trough from S_1

   b At B, two troughs will combine to produce a deep trough.
      At C, a crest combines with a trough to produce calm water.

14 Frequencies range from three hundred million million million (3×10^{20})
    hertz in the gamma region, to three thousand hertz in the radio region.

15 They travel at the speed of light; they can be reflected, refracted,
    diffracted and show interference effects.

16 a Gamma rays, X-rays, ultra-violet, visible light, infra-red, microwaves,
      radio waves.

   b ultra-violet; 30 thousand million million hertz

   c one thousand million (10^9) times; X-rays

Chapter 7

Mathematics background

You will need a scientific calculator – one with the following functions as well as the four basic arithmetical functions:

- square and square root
- log and antilog (to base 10 and base e)
- exponential
- x^y
- brackets
- sin, cos and tan

Not all of these functions will be needed for this chapter.

Significant figures

Imagine the price of identical juggling clubs in different shops is: £15.98, £13.97, £14.92, £13.99, £21.11. Now if we are going to compare prices to see which is the cheapest, we look first at the tens of pounds. This allows us to eliminate the most expensive. We now look at the pounds themselves. This allows us to eliminate the next two most expensive. We repeat this process until we are comparing the pennies, when we can work out the cheapest. This could not be succesfully done starting the other way around.

In this process we compared the **most significant figure** and worked through to the **least significant figure**. The most significant figure in any number is the one nearest the left-hand end of the number (provided it is not zero).

For example, in the number 1236.358

the 1 thousand is the	most significant figure
the 2 hundreds is the	2nd significant figure
the 3 tens is the	3rd significant figure
the 6 units is the	4th significant figure, and so on

When approximating the value of a number, it is usually written to include a specified number of significant figures. How many we use depends on the situation. We might want to quote the length of the M1 to the nearest km, the size of a snapshot to the nearest mm, the thickness of a sheet of paper to the nearest 1/100 mm.

For example, the number 1 291 573 is written as 1 290 000 to three significant figures. All the unwanted figures are turned to 0 so the number retains its value.

If when approximating to 3 sf (three significant figures) the 4th sf is a 5 or greater, then the 3rd sf is rounded up by one unit.

Express 5387.043 to 3 sf.

Here the 7 is the 4th sf and the 8 is the 3rd sf. To express this number to 3sf we need to change the 3rd sf from its value of 8 to 9. So 5387.043 is 5390 to 3 sf. (Note: To 5 sf, this would become 5387.0.)

Express 0.040 359 2 to 3 sf.

Here the 5 is the 4th sf and the 3 is the 3rd sf. So 0.040 359 2 = 0.0404 to 3 sf.

There are times when this process of rounding up can seem to reduce the number from 3 sf to 1 sf, as the following example demonstrates.

Express 59 999.0 to 3 sf.

Here the 4th sf is 9, so the 3rd sf must be rounded up.
The 3rd sf is a 9. If it is rounded up it becomes 10.
This affects the 2nd sf which must also be rounded up.
The 2nd sf is a 9. If it is rounded up, it too becomes a 10.
This affects the most significant figure. This too is rounded up.

Result: 59 999.0 to 3 sf becomes 60 000.

This result is the same as for 59 999.0 to 1 sf. But, in fact, when the answer is 60 000 to 3 sf, the first two zeros following the 6 *are* significant.

> 1 Express the following to 3 sf.
>   a 1452.3   b 9 841 667   c 41.882   d 1.999   e 0.8992
>   f 0.002 009 9
>
> 2 Write the following to 2 sf.
>   a 200.3   b 80.6   c 4.902   d 0.0205   e 0.005 96   f 99.8

Powers of ten

The Table below shows what happens as we multiply ten by ten an increasing number of times.

$$10 \times 10 = 100 = 10^2$$
$$10 \times 10 \times 10 = 1\,000 = 10^3$$
$$10 \times 10 \times 10 \times 10 = 10\,000 = 10^4$$
$$10 \times 10 \times 10 \times 10 \times 10 = 100\,000 = 10^5$$
$$10 \times 10 \times 10 \times 10 \times 10 \times 10 = 1\,000\,000 = 10^6$$

So $10^7 = 10\,000\,000$. It also follows that $2 \times 10^4 = 20\,000$. The superscripts following the 10s are the powers to which 10 has been raised. Any number can be written in this form.

> 3 Write out the values of the following:
>   a 3×10^5 b 22×10^2 c 6.3×10^7
>   d 0.4×10^3 e 1.43×10^6 f 81.89×10^2

Multiplying and dividing powers of ten

What happens if we multiply two powers of ten?
$$10^2 \times 10^3 = 100 \times 1000 = 100\,000 = 10^5$$
So, $10^2 \times 10^3 = 10^{2+3} = 10^5$
$$10^3 \times 10^4 = 1000 \times 10\,000 = 10\,000\,000 = 10^7$$
So, $10^3 \times 10^4 = 10^{3+4} = 10^7$

To multiply two numbers expressed as powers of ten together you have to add the powers of ten.

What happens if we divide powers of ten?

$$10^6/10^3 = 1\ 000\ 000/1000 = 1000 = 10^3$$

So $10^6/10^3 = 10^{6-3} = 10^3$

When dividing by powers of ten you have to subtract the powers of ten.

To multiply or divide two numbers such as 6.3×10^4 and 2.1×10^2, we can deal with each part of the number independently. So,

$$6.3 \times 10^4 \times 2.1 \times 10^2 = (6.3 \times 2.1) \times (10^4 \times 10^2) = 13.23 \times 10^6$$

and

$$6.3 \times 10^4 \div 2.1 \times 10^2 = (6.3 \div 2.1) \times (10^4 \div 10^2) = 3.0 \times 10^2$$

It is not quite so easy to see the meaning of powers that are less than 2.

$$10^3/10^2 = 1000/100 = 10$$

but, $10^3/10^2 = 10^{3-2} = 10^1$

So, 10^1 must be 10

$$10^2/10^2 = 100/100 = 1$$

but, $10^2/10^2 = 10^{2-2} = 10^0$

This means $10^0 = 1$. This is an extremely important result. In fact *any* number to the power 0 = 1.

What about powers that are less than 0?

$$10^2/10^3 = 100/1000 = 1/10 = 0.1$$

but, $10^2/10^3 = 10^{2-3} = 10^{-1}$

So, $10^{-1} = 1/10 = 0.1$

This leads to $10^{-2}\ =\ 1/100\ \ \ \ = 0.01$

$10^{-3}\ =\ 1/1000\ \ \ = 0.001$

$10^{-4}\ =\ 1/10\ 000 = 0.0001$ and so on.

Summing up:

- When 10 is raised to a power bigger than 1, this tells you the number of zeros to put after the first 1.

- When 10 is raised to a negative power (less than zero), the size of the number tells you which digit after the decimal point starts the number.

Use a calculator for questions 4 to 6, to see if your answer is the same.

4 Without using a calculator, work out the value of
  a $10^3 \times 10^3$ b $5 \times 10^2 \times 0.02$ c $8.3 \times 10^4 \times 10^7$
  d $10^2 \times 10^5 \times 10^7$ e $4 \times 10^4 \times 7 \times 10^5$

5 Without using a calculator, work out the value of
  a $10^7 \div 10^3$ b $10^4 \div 10^3$ c $5042 \div 10^2$
  d $4 \times 10^5 \div (2 \times 10^3)$ e $8 \times 10^4 \div (2 \times 10^4)$

6 Without using a calculator work out the following which involve subtracting negative numbers.
  a $10^2 \div 10^{-2}$ b $3 \div 10^{-3}$ c $3 \times 10^4 \div 10^{-6}$
  d $3 \times 10^{-3} \div (2 \times 10^{-4})$ e $0.22 \times 10^{-6} \div (0.88 \times 10^{-9})$

Standard form

Standard form is a system where all numbers are expressed as a number between 1 and 10 multiplied by a power of ten. The idea behind this is to make very large and very small numbers easier to handle. By this system,

	3129	becomes	3.129×10^3
and	0.009 723	becomes	9.723×10^{-3}

The system can also be used to help us approximate to a limited number of significant figures. For example,

	7 813 845 782	becomes	7.81×10^9 to 3 sf
and	0.000 000 041 476 38	becomes	4.148×10^{-8} to 4 sf

7 Write out the following numbers in full:
a 3.98×10^4 b 5.773×10^7 c 1.002×10^{-3}
d 8.224×10^{12} e 6.88×10^{-11} f 3.882×10^0

8 Write the following numbers in standard form to 3 sf:
a 3 155 368 b 0.000 200 553 c 1.033
d 0.000 000 053 3 e 88 545 447 822

Rearranging formulae and relationships

Whenever a mathematical formula or relationship is written down in a text book, you are always left with the impression that this is the way it should be written. However, you can rearrange it to suit your needs. You can even combine a number of them to produce a more suitable formula or relationship for yourself.

For example, we know that $V = IR$ (Ohm's Law). Suppose we know the values of V and R and wish to find I, that is, we want to make I, instead of V, the subject of the relationship.

R is multipling I, so to cancel this effect we must divide both sides of the equation by R. Thus, $V/R = IR/R$.

We can now cancel the R values on the right side of the equation, so, $V/R = I$. I is now the subject of the relationship.

When changing the subject of a mathematical formula or relationship, you need to strip off the other variables from around whatever you want to become the new subject. You need to undo or cancel any mathematical operation being done to it.

There are three pairs of mathematical operations which are in common use. Each one of the pair undoes or cancels what the other does. The three pairs are:

ADD .... SUBTRACT
MULTIPLY .... DIVIDE
SQUARE .... SQUARE-ROOT

1 Make R_1 the subject of $R_t = R_1 + R_2$.

To undo the effect of adding R_2, subtract R_2 from both sides of the equation.

$R_t - R_2 = R_1 + R_2 - R_2$

$R_t - R_2 = R_1$

2 Make t the subject of $v = d/t$.

To undo the effect of dividing by t, multiply both sides by t.

$vt = dt/t$

$vt = d$

To undo multiplying by v, divide both sides by v.

$vt/v = d/v$

$t = d/v$

3 Make v the subject of $v^2 = 2E/m$

To undo the effect of squaring v, take the square-root of both sides.

$\sqrt{v^2} = \sqrt{(2E/m)}$

$v = \sqrt{(2E/m)}$

> 9 Make each variable in turn the subject of these relationships.
>
> a $P = VI$ b $E = VIt$ c $a = v - u/t$
>
> d $s = \quad at^2$ e $E = \quad mv^2$

Combining equations

It is possible to combine two or more equations into one equation. This is generally used to simplify problems. For example,

if $a = b + c$ and $a = de$

then we can say $de = b + c$

This is possible because both of the expressions on each side of the equals sign are equal to a, and so are equal to each other.

Now we have a new single equation which does not contain the variable a. We say we have **eliminated** a. One reason for doing this is if the value of a is difficult or inconvenient to measure. We can now rearrange the combined new equation, as needed. For example,

making c the subject $c = de - b$

or making e the subject $e = (b + c)/d$

When eliminating terms, you don't have to rearrange the equations you are starting with so they both have the same subject. This may be difficult and inconvenient. Instead, you can replace one variable with its equivalent value. For example, if $g = h^2$ and $j = kg + mg^2$ and we are trying to eliminate g, there is no need to rearrange the second equation. We can, instead, replace g by h^2 everywhere we find a g. So now,

$j = kh^2 + m(h^2)^2 = kh^2 + mh^4$

Vectors

A vector is a measurement which has size and a specified direction, see Chapter 3.

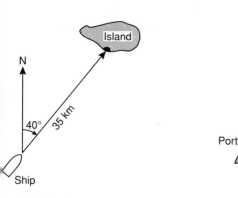

7.1 Vectors.

For example, the vector along which the ship in Fig 7.1 has to travel, to get to the island, is 40° east of north and a distance of 35 km.

Adding vectors

To add vectors together just follow one vector to its end and then follow each of the others in turn. The sum of two or more vectors is called the **resultant vector**. It is the result of combining two or more vectors, and is the vector that connects the beginning and end of the journey.

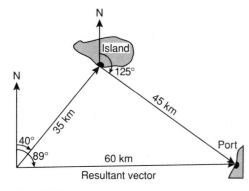

7.2 Adding vectors.

So if we look at Fig 7.2, which continues the journey of the ship in Fig 7.1, the vector from the island to the port is 125° east of north and a distance of 45 km. The resultant vector is 89° east of north and a distance of 60 km. This would give the course and distance that the ship should steer to do the journey to port directly.

The easiest way to tackle such problems is with a ruler and a protractor, using a scale diagram.

11 Express each of the following as a single resultant vector. *All* angles are made anticlockwise with the horizontal.
  a To 45 mm at 30° add 70 mm at 60°.
  b To 35 mm at 70° add 40 mm at 10°.
  c To 50 mm at 20° add 30 mm at 40° then 40 mm at 70°.

Graphs

Graphs are plotted often to try to determine if there is any relationship between two or more variables. There are three basic outcomes of plotting a graph – a straight line, a curved line, and a scatter plot.

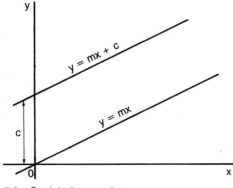

7.3   Straight line graphs.

Straight line – see Fig 7.3. This tells us that the variables x and y are related by the equation   y = mx + c.

m is the **gradient** of the line. The larger the value of m, the steeper the slope. If the sign of m is positive, the line slopes up from left to right, and if the sign of m is negative, the line slopes down from left to right.

If   c = 0,   the line passes through the origin and   y = mx. We say that x is proportional to y, often written   x ∝ y.

Curved line   A curve tells us there is a relationship between x and y but not a directly proportional one.

Scatter plot   This type of plot, with points all over the place, that cannot be joined up to form straight lines or curves, tells us there is no connection between variables x and y.

Finding gradients

The gradient of a straight line

$$\text{Gradient} = \frac{\text{the change in y}}{\text{the change in x}}$$

$$= \Delta y \, / \, \Delta x$$

For a straight line it does not matter how big Δy and Δx are; the gradient is always the same, see Fig 7.4.

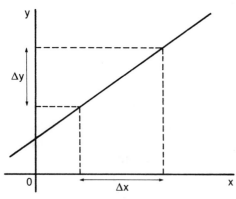

7.4   The gradient of a straight line.

The gradient of a curved line

Curved lines change their gradient all the time. We can find the gradient at any point by drawing the **tangent** to the curve at that point. We can then find the gradient of the tangent in the same way as for the straight line, see Fig 7.5.

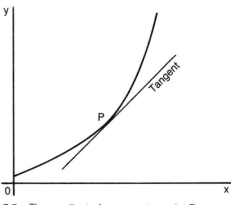

7.5   The gradient of a curve at a point P.

12 Work out what sort of relationship (if any) exists between the following variables.

a X	1	2	3	4	5	6	7
Y	3	5	7	9	11	13	15
b P	2	3	4	5	6	7	8
Q	1	2.25	4	6.25	9	12.25	16
c H	1.8	1.9	2.0	2.1	2.2	2.3	2.4
W	84	71	78	86	82	66	80

13 Plot graphs and draw the best straight lines for the following. Then work out the gradients.

a
x	2.2	2.3	2.4	2.5	2.6	2.7	2.8
y	0.31	0.33	0.34	0.36	0.37	0.39	0.4

b
x	29	34	38	42	47	55	63
y	9.7	11.3	12.7	14	15.7	18.3	21

14 Plot a graph of x against y and estimate the gradient of the curve at points   a x = 2   b x = 5 and   c x = 7.4

x	1	2	3.4	4.6	5.5	6.3	7.6	8.3	9.2
y	1	4	11.6	21.2	30.3	39.7	57.8	68.9	84.6

Answers

1 a 1450   b 9 840 000   c 41.9   d 2.00   e 0.899   f 0.002 01

2 a 200   b 81   c 4.9   d 0.021   e 0.0060   f 100

3 a 300 000   b 2200   c 63 000 000   d 400   e 1 430 000   f 8189

4 a 1 000 000 or 10^6 b 10   c 830 000 000 000 or 8.3×10^{11}
   d 100 000 000 000 000 or 10^{14} e 28 000 000 000 or 2.8×10^{10}

5 a 10 000 or 10^4 b 10   c 50.42   d 200   e 4

6 a 10 000 or 10^4 b 3 000 or 3×10^3 c 30 000 000 000 or 3×10^{10}
   d 15   e 250

7 a 39 800   b 57 730 000   c 0.001 002   d 8 224 000 000 000
   e 0.000 000 000 068 8   f 3.882

8 a 3.16×10^6 b 2.01×10^4 c 1.03×10^0 d 5.33×10^{-8} e 8.85×10^{10}

9 a $V = P/I$; $I = P/V$ b $V = E/It$; $t = E/Vt$; $t = E/VI$ c $t = (v - u)/a$;
   $v = u + at$; $u = v - at$ d $a = 2s/t^2$; $t = \sqrt{(2s/a)}$ e $m = 2E/v^2$;
   $v = \sqrt{(2E/m)}$

10 a $v = (2d/t) - u$ b $h = v^2/2g$ c i $v = 2E/p$ ii $m = p^2/2E$
    d $u = v - (Ft/m)$ e $r = F/m\omega^2$

11 a 110 mm at 48°   b 65 mm at 38° c 111 mm at 41°

12 a $y = 2x + 1$ b P is related to Q (P^2 is proportional to Q)
    c No relationship

13 a 0.16   b 0.35

14 a 2.5 b 9.2 c 14

Glossary

Acceleration: A measure of how quickly velocity changes.

Activity: The number of nuclei of a radioactive substance which decay in a given time.

Alpha radiation: Particles composed of two protons and two neutrons which are ejected from the nuclei of atoms.

Alternating current (AC): Current that regularly reverses the direction in which it flows.

Amplitude: The distance from the centre to the maximum position of an oscillation.

Angle of incidence: The angle that the ray which is incident on a surface makes with the normal.

Angle of reflection: The angle that the ray which reflects off a surface makes with the normal.

Atom: The smallest particle of any element.

Background radiation: The radiation which is always present in the environment due to emissions from rocks, the atmosphere and cosmic rays, etc.

Beta radiation: Fast-moving electrons which are ejected from the nuclei of atoms.

Conductor: A material that allows electrons to flow through it easily.

Coulomb: The unit of charge (symbol C). One coulomb is 6.25×10^{18} electrons.

Damped oscillations: Oscillations which lose energy as they vibrate.

Diffraction: The spreading out of waves as they pass through gaps or around obstacles.

Direct current (DC): Current flowing in one direction only.

Displacement: A measure of how far an object is from a given point in a specified direction.

Electric circuit: A combination of electrical components connected together to form a complete path for an electric current.

Electric current: The flow of charge (electrons).

Electromagnetic induction: The production of a current in a wire when the magnetic field across the wire changes.

Electromagnetic waves: Waves which have electric and magnetic components. They all travel at the speed of light and are grouped into a family called the electromagnetic spectrum.

Electromotive force (emf): A potential difference which drives a current around a circuit.

Electron: A negatively-charged particle found outside the nuclei of atoms. It has a mass of about 1/2000 of that of a hydrogen atom.

Energy: The ability to do work (move the point of action of a force).

Exponential decay: This means that the amount of substance reduces by a constant factor in equal time intervals, for example reducing by half in the first two minutes, then the remaining half reducing by half in the next two minutes, and so on.

Force: A push or a pull which tends to change the motion of an object.

Frequency: The number of oscillations completed in one second.

Gamma radiation: Electromagnetic waves which carry energy out of the nuclei of atoms.

Gradient: An expression of the slope of a line on a graph.

Half-life (of a radioactive substance): The time taken for the amount of radioactive material present to have reduced to one half of its original value.

Insulator: A material that strongly resists the flow of electrons through it.

Interference: The adding and cancelling out of two waves as they pass through the same area.

Interference pattern: The alternating pattern of great disturbance and calm that is produced when two waves meet.

Ion: A charged particle which is formed when electrons are removed from or added to an atom.

Ionisation energy: The energy needed to pull electrons away from the positive nucleus of an atom.

Isotopes: Atoms of the same element with different masses. They have the same number of protons and electrons but different numbers of neutrons.

Longitudinal wave: A wave in which the direction of oscillation is along the direction in which the wave is travelling.

Mass: A measure of the amount of material in an object.

Medium: The substance that a wave travels through.

Momentum: A measure of the reluctance a moving object has to stopping – the product of its mass and velocity.

Natural frequency: The frequency at which an object will vibrate freely.

Neutron: A neutral particle found in the nuclei of atoms. It has a mass almost the same as that of a hydrogen atom.

Normal (The): A straight line which is drawn at right angles to a surface, at a particular point.

Nucleus: The central part of the atom which takes up very little space but contains most of the mass of the atom.

Parallel circuit: An electric circuit where the current divides to flow through two or more components and then rejoins.

Potential difference: The difference in energy that one coulomb of charge has between two different points.

Primary coil: The input coil of a transformer.

Principle of superposition: The means by which we find the total displacement caused in a medium by more than one wave passing through – we add the separate displacements that each wave would produce.

Proton: A positively-charged particle found in the nuclei of atoms. It has a mass almost the same as that of a hydrogen atom.

Reflection: When a wave rebounds from a surface which it hits, the rebounding path makes the same angle with the surface as did the incoming path.

Refraction: The change of direction of a wave as it moves from one medium into another.

Resultant vector: The vector formed by combining two or more vectors.

Scalar: A measurement which requires only magnitude.

Secondary coil: The output coil of a transformer.

Series circuit: An electric circuit where the current must flow through each component in turn.

Simple harmonic oscillators: Oscillators which always keep the same time period even though the amplitude may change.

Speed: A measure of how fast an object is moving. Distance travelled divided by time taken.

Standard form: A system of expressing numbers as a value between 1 and 10 multiplied by a power of ten.

Time period: The time to complete one oscillation (sometimes called simply the period).

Transverse wave: A wave in which the direction of oscillation is at right angles to the direction in which the wave is travelling.

Vector: A measurement in which both magnitude and direction must be specified.

Velocity: A measure of how fast an object is moving in a specified direction.

Wavefront: Parts of the medium which are at the same point in their oscillation as a wave travels through it.

Wavelength: The distance from any point on a wave to the corresponding point on the next wave.

Work: The energy transformed by a moving force – the product of the force and the distance through which it moves in its own direction.

The Periodic Table

1 H Hydrogen 1																	2 He Helium 4
3 Li Lithium 7	4 Be Beryllium 9											5 B Boron 11	6 C Carbon 12	7 N Nitrogen 14	8 O Oxygen 16	9 F Fluorine 19	10 Ne Neon 20
11 Na Sodium 23	12 Mg Magnesium 24											13 Al Aluminium 27	14 Si Silicon 28	15 P Phosporous 31	16 S Sulphur 32	17 Cl Chlorine 35.5	18 Ar Argon 40
19 K Potassium 39	20 Ca Calcium 40	21 Sc Scandium 45	22 Ti Titanium 48	23 V Vanadium 51	24 Cr Chromium 52	25 Mn Manganese 55	26 Fe Iron 56	27 Co Cobalt 59	28 Ni Nickel 59	29 Cu Copper 63.5	30 Zn Zinc 65.4	31 Ga Gallium 70	32 Ge Germanium 73	33 As Arsenic 75	34 Se Selenium 79	35 Br Bromine 80	36 Kr Krypton 84
37 Rb Rubidium 86	38 Sr Strontium 87	39 Y Yttrium 89	40 Zr Zirconium 91	41 Nb Niobium 93	42 Mo Molybdenum 96	43 Tc Technetium 99	44 Ru Ruthenium 101	45 Rh Rhodium 103	46 Pd Palladium 106	47 Ag Silver 108	48 Cd Cadmium 112	49 In Indium 115	50 Sn Tin 119	51 Sb Antimony 122	52 Te Tellurium 128	53 I Iodine 127	54 Xe Xenon 131
55 Cs Caesium 133	56 Ba Barium 137	57 La Lanthanum 139	72 Hf Hafnium 179	73 Ta Tantalum 181	74 W Tungsten 184	75 Re Rhenium 186	76 Os Osmium 190	77 Ir Iridium 192	78 Pt Platinum 195	79 Au Gold 197	80 Hg Mercury 201	81 Tl Thallium 204	82 Pb Lead 207	83 Bi Bismuth 209	84 Po Polonium 210	85 At Astatine 210	86 Rn Radon 222
87 Fr Francium 223	88 Ra Radium 226	89 Ac Actinium 227	104 Unq Unnilquadium 261	105 Unp Unnilpentium 262	106 Unh Unnilhexium 263	107 Uns Unnilseptium 263	108 Uno Unniloctium ?	109 Une Unnilennium ?									

Key

Atomic number	
Symbol	
Name	
Relative atomic mass	

58 Ce Cerium 140	59 Pr Praseodymium 141	60 Nd Neodymium 144	61 Pm Promethium 147	62 Sm Samarium 150	63 Eu Europium 152	64 Gd Gadolinium 157	65 Tb Terbium 159	66 Dy Dysprosium 163	67 Ho Holmium 165	68 Er Erbium 167	69 Tm Thulium 169	70 Yb Ytterbium 173	71 Lu Lutetium 175
90 Th Thorium 232	91 Pa Protactinium 231	92 U Uranium 238	93 Np Neptunium 237	94 Pu Plutonium 242	95 Am Americium 243	96 Cm Curium 247	97 Bk Berkelium 245	98 Cf Californium 251	99 Es Einsteinium 254	100 Fm Fermium 253	101 Md Mendelevium 256	102 No Nobelium 254	103 Lr Lawrencium 257

- Note In most versions of the Periodic Table, including the one above, the atomic number is written at the top of the element's box and the relative atomic mass at the bottom. However, when writing the symbols of individual elements, these are usually reversed: eg $^{23}_{11}\text{Na}$